CW00766322

Simply Riemann

JEREMY GRAY

SIMPLY CHARLY
NEW YORK

Copyright © 2020 by Jeremy Gray

Cover Illustration by José Ramos
Cover Design by Scarlett Rugers

All rights reserved. No part of this publication may be reproduced, distributed, or transmitted in any form or by any means, including photocopying, recording, or other electronic or mechanical methods, without the prior written permission of the publisher, except in the case of brief quotations embodied in critical reviews and certain other noncommercial uses permitted by copyright law. For permission requests, write to the publisher at the address below.

permissions@simplycharly.com

ISBN: 978-1-943657-21-6

Brought to you by http://simplycharly.com

Contents

Praise for *Simply Riemann*   vii

Other *Great Lives*   x

Series Editor's Foreword   xi

Preface   xii

Introduction   1

1. Riemann's life and times   7
2. Geometry   42
3. Complex functions   65
4. Primes and the zeta function   88
5. Minimal surfaces   99
6. Real functions   110
7. And another thing . . .   126
8. Riemann's Legacy   128

References   145

Suggested Reading   152

About the Author   154

A Word from the Publisher   155

Praise for *Simply Riemann*

"Jeremy Gray is one of the world's leading historians of mathematics, and an accomplished author of popular science. In *Simply Riemann* he combines both talents to give us clear and accessible insights into the astonishing discoveries of Bernhard Riemann—a brilliant but enigmatic mathematician who laid the foundations for several major areas of today's mathematics, and for Albert Einstein's General Theory of Relativity. Readable, organized—and simple. Highly recommended."

—Ian Stewart, Emeritus Professor of Mathematics at Warwick University and author of *Significant Figures*

"Very few mathematicians have exercised an influence on the later development of their science comparable to Riemann's whose work reshaped whole fields and created new ones. Gray's admirable, readable account allows us to appreciate the original and profound ideas of this mathematical genius."

—Umberto Bottazzini, Professor at the University of Milan and Fellow of the American Mathematical Society

"A terrific introduction to Riemann's most characteristic ways of thinking. Gray expertly lays out the key problem situations Riemann inherited from Gauss and others, and explains the strategies and concepts that led Riemann to solve problems and create new fields of mathematics. Gray's broad historical expertise enables him to highlight just which aspects of each problem were clear to Riemann from other people's work, and pick out just what innovative turn Riemann gave to each."

—Colin McLarty, Truman P. Handy Professor and Chair of Philosophy at Case Western Reserve University

"If one had to choose a single name of a scientist who simultaneously transformed the course of mathematics, physics, and philosophy, then Bernhard Riemann should come to the forefront. Jeremy Gray's book on Riemann confirms this idea. Gray is among the rare historians for mathematics who do not only write for historians. His books are interesting for mathematicians and students in mathematics and also for the educated laymen, and this book is no exception."

—Athanase Papadopoulos, Directeur de Recherche, Centre National de la Recherche Scientifique and University of Strasbourg

"Unlike some other great mathematicians, Riemann started his math career late at the age of 25 and died at 39. He published a few papers, but his work covered many topics. Whatever he touched, he changed them in a fundamental way. What did he do? How he did it? How could he do it? In this concise scholarly biography of Riemann, one of the leading historians of mathematics of his generation gives satisfying answers to the above questions. Gray combines effectively his deep knowledge of the history of math with his insights into math to produce a fascinating narrative. Besides Riemann, the reader can also learn about stories of other great people such as Gauss and of the scientific community at Riemann's time."

—Lizhen Ji, Professor of Mathematics at University of Michigan

"For readers acquainted with calculus, but not necessarily much more, Gray has written an engrossing account of Riemann's revolutionary contributions to mathematics. Riemann lived and breathed mathematics, and Gray rightly makes mathematics the story of Riemann's life. He also brings to light the origins of many fields of modern mathematics."

—John Stillwell, author of *The Real Numbers* and Professor of Mathematics, University of San Francisco

"In this brief but concentrated account of the life and mathematical works of the great German mathematician Bernhard Riemann, readers will find a lively, detailed analysis of the ethereal realms of mathematics to which Riemann made fundamental contributions. Here Jeremy Gray writes primarily for mathematical readers, who will appreciate the frequent asides, usually prefaced by "More about the mathematics," that help to explain the significance (or difficulties) with what has just been discussed. In the end, readers will come away from *Simply Riemann* with a better understanding of some of the most important advances that were made in mathematics in the nineteenth century, when the face of the subject underwent profound changes, many of them due to Bernhard Riemann, tragically dead all too soon at age thirty-nine."

—Joseph W. Dauben, Distinguished Professor of History and History of Science, City University of New York

"Bernhard Riemann is a towering figure, without doubt, one of the greatest mathematicians. He contributed profound ideas to many areas of mathematics, but above all, he brought a revolution to the most classical one, geometry. Riemann had wide interests, including very especially physics and philosophy, and this enabled him to become one of the architects of modern mathematics. Thus a book on Riemann for the general reader is a great idea—and Jeremy Gray is admirably suited to write such a book."

—José Ferreirós, Professor of Logic and Philosophy of Science, Universidad de Sevilla

Other *Great Lives*

Simply Austen by Joan Klingel Ray
Simply Beckett by Katherine Weiss
Simply Beethoven by Leon Plantinga
Simply Chekhov by Carol Apollonio
Simply Chomsky by Raphael Salkie
Simply Chopin by William Smialek
Simply Darwin by Michael Ruse
Simply Descartes by Kurt Smith
Simply Dickens by Paul Schlicke
Simply Dirac by Helge Kragh
Simply Einstein by Jimena Canales
Simply Eliot by Joseph Maddrey
Simply Euler by Robert E. Bradley
Simply Faulkner by Philip Weinstein
Simply Fitzgerald by Kim Moreland
Simply Freud by Stephen Frosh
Simply Gödel by Richard Tieszen
Simply Hegel by Robert L. Wicks
Simply Hitchcock by David Sterritt
Simply Joyce by Margot Norris
Simply Machiavelli by Robert Fredona
Simply Napoleon by J. David Markham & Matthew Zarzeczny
Simply Nietzsche by Peter Kail
Simply Proust by Jack Jordan
Simply Sartre by David Detmer
Simply Tolstoy by Donna Tussing Orwin
Simply Stravinsky by Pieter van den Toorn
Simply Turing by Michael Olinick
Simply Wagner by Thomas S. Grey
Simply Wittgenstein by James C. Klagge

Series Editor's Foreword

S imply Charly's "Great Lives" series offers brief but authoritative introductions to the world's most influential people—scientists, artists, writers, economists, and other historical figures whose contributions have had a meaningful and enduring impact on our society.

Each book provides an illuminating look at the works, ideas, personal lives, and the legacies these individuals left behind, also shedding light on the thought processes, specific events, and experiences that led these remarkable people to their groundbreaking discoveries or other achievements. Additionally, every volume explores various challenges they had to face and overcome to make history in their respective fields, as well as the little-known character traits, quirks, strengths, and frailties, myths, and controversies that sometimes surrounded these personalities.

Our authors are prominent scholars and other top experts who have dedicated their careers to exploring each facet of their subjects' work and personal lives.

Unlike many other works that are merely descriptions of the major milestones in a person's life, the "Great Lives" series goes above and beyond the standard format and content. It brings substance, depth, and clarity to the sometimes-complex lives and works of history's most powerful and influential people.

We hope that by exploring this series, readers will not only gain new knowledge and understanding of what drove these geniuses, but also find inspiration for their own lives. Isn't this what a great book is supposed to do?

Charles Carlini, Simply Charly
New York City

Preface

This book offers an introduction to the work of Bernhard Riemann (September 17, 1826 – July 20, 1866), one of the most profound and influential mathematicians of the 19th century, whose insights continue to reshape mathematics to this day.

It is fitting that Riemann should be included in the Simply Charly *Great Lives* series, alongside other eminent personalities like Kurt Gödel and Ludwig Wittgenstein, though placing him there has naturally required some compromises. I took the challenge as an opportunity to discuss Riemann's life, times, and the world in which a quiet university professor could accomplish such radical things in the fields of differential geometry, number theory, and complex analysis, among his other achievements. But I have also tried to say something about mathematics as he saw it and as he helped it become.

Riemann's genius was to be very clear regarding what a piece of mathematics was about, to strip it of unnecessary presumptions, and to show how the clarity thus obtained was productive. He saw mathematics as a system of concepts, rather than merely as a battery of formulae and techniques. His concepts are often very general, which accounts for their lasting effect, and his insights are often deep: he could see how his ideas inter-related and use them to resolve outstanding problems in the subject. His challenge was to bring out those concepts, which are often very simple and natural, and to show them at work.

What mathematics is involved here? Little more than the skills needed to read a map, a small amount of calculus, a knowledge of what complex numbers are, a liking for geometry, and, in the final chapter, taking pleasure in unexpected detail. And, courtesy of Riemann and any great mathematician, the boldness to see where these ideas can take you.

I would like to thank my Open University colleague June Barrow-

Green for years of helpful conversations and good advice; Erhard Scholz for sharing his knowledge of Riemann, geometry, physics, and much else; Lizhen Ji and Athanase Papadopoulos for their comments on a draft that removed many errors; Mario Micallef for many discussions about geometry; and numerous mathematicians and historians of mathematics for conveying their excitement for mathematics and the fascinating riches it contains.

Jeremy Gray
London, England

Introduction

Figure 1. *Georg Friedrich Bernhard Riemann*
(1826–1866)

W hy should we care about Bernhard Riemann? My answer is: because he is one of the great mathematicians, and was a major influence on the move towards a conceptual, modern mathematics. Paradoxically, the highly conceptual character of his work gives us an excellent opportunity to peer over his shoulder and ponder about what makes some questions in mathematics important, and how we can think mathematically before and after we calculate. In many ways, it is easier, and more exciting, to follow his ideas than those of the virtuoso calculators with symbols and formulae who practiced a form of mathematics he appreciated but was keen to get beyond.

Riemann only lived to 39 years of age, dying in 1866. But despite his brief lifespan, his name became attached to many important topics in 20th- and 21st-century mathematics: geometers and cosmologists speak of Riemannian geometry; many people have heard of the Riemann zeta function and the celebrated Riemann hypothesis, often called the most important unsolved problem in mathematics; mathematical analysts often refer to the idea of a Riemann surface (including the Riemann sphere).

The range of Riemann's interests was remarkable. Although his best work was in mathematics, he himself said that his principal concern was in physics—the propagation of heat, light, electromagnetism, and gravitation. To bring his ideas into focus, he drew deeply on contemporary philosophy, and undoubtedly these concepts shaped his rewrite of the nature of geometry.

The philosophy of Johann Friedrich Herbart influenced Riemann's mathematics. Herbart became Immanuel Kant's successor as professor at the University of Königsberg in 1808 and divided his time there between philosophy and pedagogy until he was appointed professor of philosophy at the University of Göttingen, where he remained until he died in 1841 at the age of 65. While in Königsberg, he wrote his major work, *Psychology as Science Newly Founded on Experience, Metaphysics, and Mathematics.*

In this book, Herbart argued that experience and metaphysics are equal partners. He explained, in language drawn from contemporary applied mathematics, how the mind deals with experience and forms concepts, how it constructs visual space, how it uses repeated sensations to form memories, and much else. Although a Kantian in some respects, Herbart disagreed with Kant in many ways. In particular, he was willing to identify knowledge of appearances with knowledge of the thing in itself. But for Herbart, what was real was also discrete, and the mind generates the concept of a continuum because it can postulate continuous relations between the discrete points. This intelligible space is the source of our intuitions of Space with its familiar geometric properties, and so for Herbart Space was not an a priori form of intuition as it was for Kant. Instead, it was a derived and constructed intuition.

At times, Riemann was critical of Herbart's work, but he valued it highly. He wrote (*Werke*, p. 539) that he could agree with almost all of Herbart's earliest research, but not with his later speculations at certain essential points to do with his *Naturphilosophie* (Natural Philosophy) and psychology. Elsewhere in the *Nachlass* (a collection of manuscripts and other notes left when the author dies), he wrote (quoted in Scholz 1982, 414) that he was Herbartian in epistemology but not in ontology.

Riemann regarded natural science as an attempt to comprehend nature by precise concepts. Herbart had shown that all concepts that help us understand the world arise by refining earlier concepts. They need not be derived a priori, as with the Kantian categories. But Riemann said (*Werke*, 554) it is because concepts originate in comprehending what sense-perception provides that "*their significance can be established in a manner adequate for natural science*" (emphasis in original).

For Riemann, a conception of the world is correct, "when the coherence of our ideas corresponds to the coherence of things," and this coherence of things will be obtained "from the coherence of phenomena" (Riemann *Werke*, 555). So an internally self-consistent set of ideas is to be matched somehow to the coherent phenomena. But Riemann largely skipped Herbart's description of how the coherent system of ideas about space is generated from experience and went straight to the generation of geometric concepts in mathematics. He even allowed that Space could be discrete, inspired perhaps by Herbart's opinion that it is only intelligible Space that is continuous. However, he dropped Herbart's view that Space was necessarily three-dimensional, and was insistent on thinking geometrically about any number of variables.

Mathematics, in Herbart's view, was more like philosophy than science, and Riemann's position on science and mathematics was heavily conceptual. One thorough study of Herbart's influence concluded that Riemann's views on mathematics "seem to have been deepened and clarified by his extensive studies of Herbart's philosophy. Moreover, without this orientation, Riemann might never have formulated his profound and innovative concept of a manifold" (Scholz 1982, 426).

The major issues in the theoretical physics of Riemann's time had to do with gravitation and electromagnetism. These were taken, controversially, to involve action at a distance, perhaps mediated by an all-pervading ether that, whatever it might be, gave substance to Space. These questions interested the young Riemann deeply. While finishing his post-doctoral work in Göttingen in the early 1850s, he also worked in the laboratory of physicist Wilhelm Weber, a friend and colleague of the eminent mathematician Carl Friedrich Gauss. Riemann worked there on "the connection between electricity, light, and magnetism" (Riemann *Werke*, 580). He drafted a paper drawing on his reading of the work of Isaac Newton, Leonhard Euler, and, more surprisingly, Herbart, in which Herbart's plenum was transformed into a universe filled with a substance flowing through atoms and out of the material world. Stresses and strains in this substance (a species of ether) show up as deformations of the local metric. This variation in the metric would, in turn, be felt by a particle as a force, and by resisting this force, the particle might move through Space. However, he found that he could not make these ideas work, and the paper was abandoned.

He returned to the theme of gravitation and light some years later, this time coming up with a theory in which motion through Space was explained purely in terms of relations defined infinitesimally. Nothing was published, but Riemann did discuss the properties of the ether in his lectures of 1861, published by the Göttingen mathematician Karl Hattendorff, in 1876. In this version, variations in the density of the ether would be responsible for electro-static and electro-dynamic effects.

The principal influence of these speculations was not in physics, but in the theory of geometry that Riemann set out in his post-doctoral (Habilitation) lecture. There, the idea of local distortions of space leads naturally to the idea of a variable metric on a mathematically defined space. In a way, his work dramatically raised the possibility that there might be many forms of mathematics, all potentially valid, or at least useful in physics.

The structure of this book

We start with a chapter on the major influences on the mathematical world into which Riemann was born. It would over-simplify, but not by much, to sum that up in a word: Gauss. As the standard biographies of Gauss—(Dunnington 1955/2004) and (Bühler 1981)—make clear, he was a German mathematician whose brilliance earned him the title of the last Prince of Mathematicians. His work between 1799, when he turned 22, and 1855, when he died, set the agenda for all who followed him, Riemann included. Riemann's work in geometry and mathematical analysis would have been impossible without Gauss's insights. But there were other influences in the generation between Gauss and Riemann, among them that of Peter Gustav Lejeune Dirichlet, who not only had a fine eye for rigor in mathematics, but was also a personal help to Riemann, and Dirichlet's friend Carl Gustav Jacob Jacobi. Behind them all stood the figure of Leonhard Euler, the dominant mathematician of the 18th century, many of whose works Riemann came to know very well.

Then we turn to Riemann's work on geometry: the creation of infinitely many geometries that might be physically plausible, mathematically useful, or just downright interesting.

Then we look at the subject on which he wrote the most: the theory of functions of a complex variable. This is now a standard branch of mathematical analysis. At the time, it was an entirely new field, one that Riemann's ideas helped to shape, ideas that were challenged root and branch by his rivals in Berlin—Karl Weierstrass and Hermann Amandus Schwarz. From this work, Riemann proposed the celebrated "Riemann hypothesis," as we shall see in the next chapter, and, in the chapter after that, to break open the unsolved Plateau problem about surfaces of minimal area.

The following chapter shows how markedly Dirichlet influenced Riemann. In it, we look at Riemann's paper on what are called trigonometric series. It is, as Riemann observed, partly an inquiry into the limits of the calculus: can there be functions to which the calculus does not apply, and if so, what can we say about them? After that, we will look briefly at some of Riemann's achievements that cannot be described here, and the book concludes with a discussion of his legacy and some of the work that it has inspired.

Pre-requisites

I have made every effort to keep the text to as elementary a level as possible, but I assume readers know a little coordinate geometry, that they know what complex numbers are (and are comfortable thinking of them as points in the plane), that they are willing to assume that there are functions of a complex variable, although they may know nothing about them, and that they have met the elementary calculus. Topics that go beyond this are discussed in four boxes and at the end of Chapter 4. The currency for enjoying this book is that the more you know in these final sections, the less you have to take on trust.

1. Riemann's life and times

Georg Bernhard Friedrich Riemann was born on September 17, 1826, the second of six children. As the author Detlef Laugwitz describes in the standard biography of the mathematician (Laugwitz 1999), Riemann's father was a pastor in Breselenz near Dannenberg in Hanover, which was then a poor part of Germany on the Elbe river. Young Riemann grew up as an introverted child who found it difficult to get close to people. Until he turned 14, he was taught at home and in the village school in Quickborn, where his family had moved, and he was unhappy when he was sent away to school in Hanover and Lüneburg. He never found it easy to express himself, but C. Schmalfuss, the Director of the school in Lüneburg, soon realized that the boy had a talent for mathematics and gave him books to foster this innate gift. When he received Adrien-Marie Legendre's *Théorie des Nombres* (Number Theory), an old-fashioned but demanding book by a Frenchman who had been a leading mathematician in his time, Riemann returned it within a week, saying "This is a wonderful book; I know it by heart."

In September 1846, Riemann went to the University in Göttingen. There, he quickly transferred from theology, which his father had wanted him to study, to mathematics, a subject that matched his evident ability. Gauss still worked there, but he only taught elementary statistics, so Riemann availed himself of the right of every German student to study anywhere in Germany and went to the University of Berlin during Easter of 1847. The university had been founded by Alexander von Humboldt in 1809 as part of a move to help Prussia recover from the shock of being overrun by Napoleon's armies, and it was being built up as the leading university in the state. Humboldt brought Dirichlet there when he heard of his great merits as a mathematician, and it was Dirichlet who first taught Riemann advanced mathematics.

Dirichlet lectured on number theory, definite integrals, and partial differential equations. His friend Jacobi also taught there, lecturing on analytical mechanics and higher algebra. These two men had almost single-handedly modernized the study of mathematics in Germany; Dirichlet, in particular, was fully aware of the changes being wrought in Paris, then the center of the mathematical world.

Riemann learned a lot in the two years he spent in Berlin, but he returned to Göttingen after the political upheavals that occurred in Europe in 1848. He took his degree there, combining his studies with readings in philosophy and physics. He particularly enjoyed a course in experimental physics given by Gauss's colleague Wilhelm Weber and joined the seminar on mathematical physics. He then immediately embarked on his doctorate, which he took in 1851. After that, the only formal qualification left to get was the so-called Habilitation, which was a necessary and sufficient condition to teach at any German university (it did not imply that you would also be paid).

Once back in Göttingen, Riemann's life proceeded quietly, in ways that the following chapters document. In the autumn of 1852, Dirichlet visited Göttingen and, to Riemann's delight, spent two hours talking to him, discussing his doctoral thesis, and giving him advice about the Habilitation that he was preparing for. Riemann wrote to his father that Dirichlet had been "extremely friendly" towards him, and they met again at Weber's house later in the week. One wonders if Dirichlet was visiting Göttingen with his own prospects in mind; in any event, when Gauss died in 1855, Dirichlet succeeded him, which must have pleased Riemann greatly. By then, Riemann had passed his Habilitation exam triumphantly and was already lecturing on an informal basis at the university. With Dirichlet's arrival, Riemann got a small salary but attempts to get him appointed as a junior professor failed.

Riemann now devoted himself to his research and published two major papers in 1857, one on a particular ordinary differential equation that Gauss had studied, and the other on what is called the theory of Abelian functions (as we discuss below). The effort of working out his new approach to these subjects, resolving problems that had defeated his illustrious predecessors and then explaining what he had done in enough detail to be understood completely exhausted him, and he became depressed. His spirits were restored during a walking holiday in the Harz mountains with his friend, the young mathematician Richard Dedekind; on his return, he was finally appointed a junior professor.

Family misfortunes then disrupted Riemann's life. His father and one of his sisters had died in 1855. His three remaining sisters had then gone to live with their brother Wilhelm, but he too died in the winter of 1857-1858. Following these tragedies, Bernhard took responsibility for the family in March of 1858, and they came to live with him in Göttingen. Almost at once, a second sister died, and for several months he and his remaining siblings were burdened with heavy grief.

In 1859, Dirichlet died unexpectedly. In the round of appointments that followed, Riemann was made a full professor, but in 1862 his health collapsed from pleurisy; from then on, managing his illness was a top priority. Soon it became clear that it was a matter of managing his decline. He spent as much time as he could in or near Pisa, where Eugenio Beltrami, the Italian mathematician whose name has become most closely tied to Riemann's, became a professor in 1863. He continued to generate ideas, but his time was running out. On July 20, 1866, Riemann died at the age of 39, near Lake Maggiore.

One of the most important Italian mathematicians to visit Riemann in his final years was Enrico Betti, who had just become the Director of the important Scuola Normale Superiore in Pisa and had also been elected to the Italian parliament in 1862. He was dedicated to improving mathematics in Italy's schools and universities and was particularly interested in extending Riemann's topological ideas. He also worked on mechanics and theoretical physics.

Gauss

On May 10, 1854, Riemann was a happy man. He had just successfully completed the Habilitation examination that allowed him to teach at a German University, a test that he had repeatedly called "a halter round his neck," and his examiner had been none other than the greatest mathematician of the day, Carl Friedrich Gauss.

Figure 2. Carl Friedrich Gauss (1777-1855)

The examination had gone well. Gauss talked with uncharacteristic excitement to his colleague Wilhelm Weber about it afterwards, struck by the profundity of the ideas that Riemann had put forward. As was the custom, Riemann had proposed three topics that he could be examined on, but unusually Gauss had chosen not the first of these but the third, curious to know what Riemann had to say on one of his own favorite subjects—the foundations of geometry. The answer had exceeded his expectations; Riemann had extended his ideas far beyond anything he had ever contemplated.

The examination almost perfectly symbolizes the transition from one generation to the next—Gauss handed over the subject he had dominated for 50 years to the person best suited to lead mathematics into the second half of the 19th century. If any two mathematicians can stand for their times, no one would dispute the claims of these two.

Gauss had made his name in 1801, at the age of 24. In that year, he re-wrote number theory, making it into the subject that almost all later German mathematicians have wanted to contribute to; he also found the lost asteroid Ceres.

Ceres had been discovered not long before by the Italian astronomer Giuseppe Piazzi. It was the first asteroid to be found, and its orbit lay in the puzzling gap between Mars and Jupiter, so its discovery caused much excitement. Piazzi tracked it for 41 nights until it passed behind the Sun before publishing his observations and challenging the scientific community to determine where and when it would reappear.

It is a non-trivial task to derive an orbit from a collection of observations. All will be slightly wrong. Some, taken early in the morning or late in the evening when Ceres was barely visible and when it was near the horizon, could be totally wrong. Traditional methods involved finding the most plausible or typical observations and calculating an orbit from them. Gauss took the lot, invented the statistical method of least squares, and came up with the only prediction good enough to allow Ceres to be found again. Because he had been the only one to get it right, he won the astronomers' respect. Indeed, for a long time afterwards, Gauss worked as an astronomer. He was one of those rare mathematicians who have a highly-developed ability at mental arithmetic, and he liked the long calculations astronomy involved. The work was well-respected in society, and he regarded it as one of the ways in which he repaid his debt to the Duke of Brunswick, who had paid for his education at the Collegium Carolinum for the four years before Gauss went to Göttingen in 1795.

But the work on number theory was even more influential. Interest in the properties of whole numbers (the integers) has a long history—results about prime numbers occupy three books of Euclid's *Elements*. In the 17th century, Pierre de Fermat had discovered many intriguing results about them, such as the fact that every prime number of the form $4n + 1$ for some integer n is a sum of two squares. For example, $5 = 4 \times 1 + 1 = 2^2 + 1^2$ and $13 = 4 \times 3 + 1 = 3^2 + 2^2$. He also had a proof that there are no integers x, y, z greater than 1, such that

$$x^4 + y^4 = z^4.$$

He had even incautiously committed himself to the statement that there are no integers x, y, z greater than 1, such that

$$x^n + y^n = z^n.$$

for any integer n other than 1 or 2. This claim became known as Fermat's Last Theorem and was only proved by Andrew Wiles and Richard Taylor in 1995.

Fermat, however, did not succeed in interesting his contemporaries in number theory, and it was not until Leonhard Euler in the mid-18th century that the subject drew serious attention. Many of Euler's gifted explorations were systematized and then worked over again by Joseph-Louis Lagrange. But Gauss wholly reworked the subject, from the simple idea of modular arithmetic to the deepest theorems about the representation of numbers by quadratic forms, and added many new ideas.

Over the years after this dramatic debut, Gauss worked on differential equations, on potential theory (constructing with Weber the first electric telegraph), and in particular, did the work on geometry that we shall look at next.

Gauss on geometry

Early in the 17th century, René Descartes's ideas about geometry—the origin of today's coordinate geometry—had greatly enriched the study of curves in the plane. The calculus initiated by Isaac Newton and Gottfried Leibniz a generation later further advanced the study of curves.

But even in the 18th century, the best mathematicians did little to produce a comparable theory of surfaces. It is easy to see why. The simplest equation for a surface would be something like the equation of a paraboloid (see Figure 3).

$$z = x^2 + y^2.$$

More generally, it would be an equation of the form

$$z = f(x, y),$$

which gives the height z above the (x, y) plane of each point (x, y, z) on the surface as a function f of x and y. In this formulation, z is a function of the two variables x and y, so if the calculus is to be used, it has to be a calculus of two variables. Such a calculus was created in the 18th century, but it is naturally more complicated than the calculus of functions of a single variable (and pictures of any complexity are hard to draw).

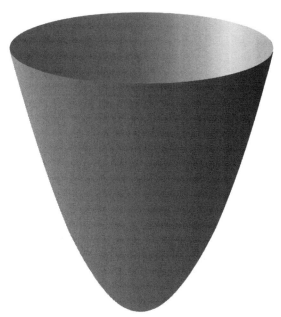

Figure 3. A paraboloid

More surfaces can be written in the way we write the equation of a sphere with center the origin and radius r:

$$x^2 + y^2 + z^2 = r^2.$$

Indeed, generally an equation of the form

$$F(x, y, z) = 0$$

will define a surface. The extra difficulty here is that the variables x, y, and z are tangled up together, which can make it hard to extract the information we want.

In the 1810s and 1820s, Gauss was drawn into the survey of Hanover that the local Prince wanted. At first, he resisted, but pressure was brought to bear via the King of England, who was a senior member of the Hanoverian royal family, and finally, Gauss had no choice. He was a professional astronomer, German astronomical instruments were the best in the world at the time, and this was the first opportunity to produce the most accurate survey of a large area of the globe so that Gauss could see some point to it. The survey was even extended to the territories of southern Denmark that were later to be annexed by the Prussians as part of Bismarck's campaign in the 1860s to unify Germany, presumably using maps that Gauss had helped to draw up.

Gauss participated in every aspect of the survey, going into the countryside to manage the measuring of distances and angles, and transforming the raw data into practical information. It has been estimated that the data consisted of about a million numbers—big data indeed in the time before computers. But what Gauss achieved is even more remarkable: the first full understanding of what it takes for a map from one surface to another to represent angles correctly and the discovery of the concept of the intrinsic curvature of a surface that was to change the study of surfaces completely.

Surfaces and maps

Cartographers already knew a lot about how to depict a part of the Earth's surface, thought of as a region on a sphere, on a flat page. In 1775, the great and prolific mathematician Leonhard Euler had indicated what the mathematics involved, and his Swiss contemporary Johann Lambert had gone into some detail about the implications for actual cartography (several of Lambert's ideas are still in use today). Lagrange had then extended Euler's work to deal with the relatively recent discovery that the Earth is more accurately thought of as a sphere flattened slightly at the poles.

Euler had even used his analysis to prove what every cartographer suspected: that there could be no map of the Earth's surface onto a plane that is accurate in every respect. Some maps send curves of shortest length on the sphere to straight lines in the plane; there are maps that send angles to equal angles, and there are maps that scale all areas by the same amount. But there can be no map that does all of these at once.

The most important problem with maps concerns how they represent distances.

Suppose we wish to go hiking. Even in the age of GPS and other tracking and location systems, we consult a detailed map. We measure each part of the route in inches, and then consult the scale that tells us how many inches on the map correspond to how many miles on the ground. This is given by a rule that depends on how the map has been constructed. No map is perfect, and the rule may even produce different conversion factors from point to point. (In fact, it certainly will, but ingenious cartographers have devised map projections that usually make these corrections unnecessary on any given sheet of the atlas.)

Therefore, we are familiar with the idea of a rule that says what real distances are given distances on a sheet in an atlas. Let's think about these rules a little more. Most maps use coordinates that are referred to as true North (the y-axis, if you like) and East (the x-axis).

The system of coordinates on a surface that we are most familiar with is that of longitude and latitude on the Earth, which we shall take to be a sphere of radius R.

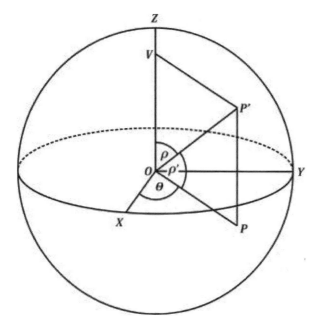

Figure 4. Latitude, longitude, and co-latitude

Latitude and longitude coordinates are displayed in Figure 4. It shows a sphere of radius R with its center O at the origin of a system of (x, y, z) coordinates. We consider a point P on the sphere and suppose it sits vertically above a point P' on the equatorial plane.

The longitude of the point P is the angle θ between the x-axis and the line OP'. The latitude of the point P is the angle ρ' between OP' and OP. We shall also need the point V on the z-axis that has the same height as P (and so $VP = OP' = R\cos\rho'$, and $VO = PP' = R\sin\rho'$).

It turns out to be convenient sometimes to use not the latitude but what is called the co-latitude, which is the angle between the z-axis and the line OP'. As a result, we have, $\rho + \rho' = \pi/2$, and so $\cos\rho = \sin\rho'$ and $\sin\rho = \cos\rho'$.

The way the longitude and latitude coordinates of the point P

relate to the (x, y, z) coordinates of P is found as follows: the point P' has coordinates $(r \cos \theta, r \sin \theta, 0)$, where the length OP' is $r = R \cos \rho'$. The height PP' is $R \sin \rho'$. So the (x, y, z) coordinates of the point P' are

$$R(\cos \rho' \cos \theta, R \cos \rho' \sin \theta, R \sin \rho').$$

In terms of the colatitude, this is

$$R(\sin \rho \cos \theta, R \sin \rho \sin \theta, R \cos \rho).$$

Now we have a simple map of the sphere onto the plane with coordinates (θ, ρ') obtained by associating the point P on the sphere with the point (θ, ρ') on the plane. Or, more precisely, with the region of the plane in which

$$-\pi < \theta \le 0 \quad \text{and} \quad -\pi/2 < \rho' < \pi/2.$$

This forgets about the north and south poles, and thereby avoids some mathematical complications that we do not need here.

To see how distance depends on latitude and longitude on the sphere, we consider in Figure 5 a very small triangle PAB on the sphere which is obtained as follows: the point A has the same latitude as P, but a longitude of $\theta + d\theta$, where $d\theta$ is a very small angle. The point B has the same longitude as P, but a latitude of $\rho' + d\rho'$, where $d\rho'$ is a very small angle.

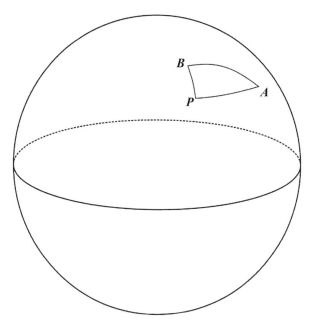

Figure 5. Distances on the sphere

We are interested in the length of the side AB. There are numerous ways of calculating it. The simplest is to observe that the arc PA lies on a circle of constant latitude and radius $VP = R\cos\rho'$ and so it has a length of $R\cos\rho' d\theta$. Similarly, the arc PB lies on a circle of constant longitude and radius R, and so it has a length of $Rd\rho'$. Then, if the sides PA and PB are very small, the triangle PAB can be regarded as approximately a right-angled triangle and by the Pythagorean theorem

$$AB^2 = r^2(d\rho'^2 + \cos^2\rho' d\theta^2).$$

This tells us that with this particular map, a distance of AB on the page of the atlas corresponds to different distances on the sphere, and indeed in a way that depends on the latitude of the points on the sphere but not their longitudes.

But longitude and latitude coordinates are just one system of coordinates on one particular surface. Every cartographer knows that there are many useful systems of coordinates on the sphere, each with their own advantages and disadvantages, and for the general study of surfaces, it will surely be best to find the simplest system for each individual surface that is being studied. Gauss, therefore, embarked on a general study of coordinate systems on a general surface.

He defined a surface as the collection of points in space with coordinates.

$$(x(u,v), y(u,v), z(u,v))$$

Given by three functions $x(u,v)$, $y(u,v)$, and $z(u,v)$ of u and v. We can also interpret this as saying that each point on the surface—which has an x, a y, and a z coordinate, also has a u and a v coordinate, as shown in Figure 6, in which curves with a constant u coordinate run upwards (one is shown in red) and curves with a constant v coordinate (one is shown in green) run left to right.

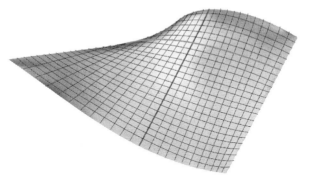

Figure 6. A (u,v) coordinate grid on a surface

Let us see how small distances in the (u,v) plane correspond to distances on the surface. In Figure 7, to go from one point A to another nearby point B, we can suppose that A has coordinates (u,v) and B, being nearby, has coordinates $(u+du, v+dv)$. Here, the symbols du and dv are traditional symbols for very small, one could almost say infinitesimal distances.

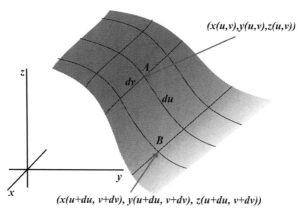

Figure 7. Distances between points on a surface in (u, v) coordinates

To find how far it is from A to B, we note that the increase in the first coordinate is du, and this takes us to the point C with coordinates $(u + du, v)$ The increase in the second coordinate is dv, and this takes us from C to B. So, we have a little triangle ACB right-angled at C, with sides AC of length du, CB of length dv, and AB of length $d\sigma$, and so, by the Pythagorean theorem,

$$d\sigma^2 = du^2 + dv^2.$$

What about the corresponding distances on the ground? Now we need to know where the corresponding points are. The points on the ground corresponding to A or (u, v) and C or $(u + du, v + dv)$ have coordinates

$$(x(u, v), y(u, v), z(u, v))$$

and

$$(x(u + du, v + dv), y(u + du, v + dv), z(u + du, v + dv)).$$

How far apart are they?

Now, we have a little right-angled triangle in three-dimensional space, and the Pythagorean theorem says that this distance, ds, is given by the square root of

$$(x(u+du, v+dv) - x(u, v))^2 + (y(u+du, v+dv) - y(u, v))^2 + (z(u+du, v+dv) - z(u, v))^2.$$

Ideally, we want this in terms of u and v. We are going to leave Gauss alone to work this out (see Box 1) and jump to his answer:

$$ds^2 = E(u, v)du^2 + 2F(u, v)dudv + G(u, v)dv^2,$$

where E, F, and G are functions of u and v that depend on the surface we are considering (and so on the functions x, y, and z).

An important thing to note is that $EG - F^2$ is always positive, a fact that follows mathematically from the way we have set this up. This means that the distance between any two points is always positive, as it should be.

Box 1: Gauss's general form for a metric:

Here's how to calculate Gauss's formula for the metric on a surface. The surface in three-dimensional space is specified by the (x, y, z) coordinates of points on it, which are given by the functions $x(u, v)$, $y(u, v)$, and $z(u, v)$.

The metric in space is given by the formula

$$ds^2 = dx^2 + dy^2 + dz^2.$$

We need to introduce the so-called partial derivatives of x, written x_u, and x_v. Of these, x_u, often also written $\frac{\partial x}{\partial u}$, is the derivative of x with respect to u holding v

---

fixed, so it expresses the rate of increase of x at a point in the u direction. Similarly, x_v or $\frac{\partial x}{\partial v}$ is the derivative of x with respect to v, holding u fixed, and it expresses the rate of increase of x at a point in the v direction.

We have $dx = x_u du + x_v dv$. So

$$dx^2 = x_u^2 du^2 + 2x_u x_v du dv + x_v^2 dv^2,$$

and similarly

$$dy^2 = y_u^2 du^2 + 2y_u y_v du dv + y_v^2 dv^2,$$
$$dz^2 = z_u^2 du^2 + 2z_u z_v du dv + z_v^2 dv^2.$$

Adding these up, we get

$$ds^2 = dx^2 + dy^2 + dz^2 =$$

$$(x_u^2 du^2 + y_u^2 du^2 + z_u^2 du^2)du^2 + 2(x_u x_v + y_u y_v + z_u z_v)du dv +$$
$$(x_v^2 + y_v^2 + z_v^2)dv^2.$$

Gauss defined

$$E(u,v) = x_u^2 du^2 + y_u^2 du^2 + z_u^2 du^2, \quad F(u,v) = x_u x_v + y_u y_v + z_u z_v,$$
$$G(u,v) = x_v^2 + y_v^2 + z_v^2,$$

and so wrote the metric as

$$ds^2 = E(u,v)du^2 + 2F(u,v)du dv + G(u,v)dv^2.$$

This formula was known to Euler and others before Gauss, but Gauss had given it a powerful new interpretation.

What does this formula for ds^2 say? It says, for example, that a step of du in the u direction on the map corresponds to a distance of $\sqrt{E(u,v)}du$ on the ground, and similarly that a step of dv in the

v direction on the map corresponds to a distance of $\sqrt{G(u,v)}\,du$ on the ground. This is the general form of the scale factor that was mentioned before.

Now if you want to know how far it is from one point on a surface to another, say from the point (u_0, v_0) to the point (u_1, v_1) along a curve that joins them, you calculate the expression for ds at every point on the curve and 'add them up'—mathematically, you evaluate the integral $\int ds$ along the curve from the initial to the final point.

Gauss used his general formula for a metric to explain a lot of things. Suppose, for example, that the curves along which u varies but v is kept constant (say $v = v_0$) and the curves along which v varies but u is kept constant (say $u = u_0$) meet at right angles on the map. Do their images on the ground also meet at right angles?

This is true of the latitude and longitude curves on the sphere. Points with the same degree of latitude lie on the sphere in a circle parallel to the equator, and points with the same degree of longitude lie on great circles joining the poles, and these meet at right angles, as you can see by rotating the sphere about its north-south axis.

But it is not always true, as in the case of (x, y) coordinates on the sphere (to be unambiguous, we consider only the upper hemisphere, where $z>0$). In Figure 8, points on the sphere that have the same x coordinate lie on a circle cut out by a plane parallel to the (y, z) plane, and points on the sphere that have the same y coordinate lie on a circle cut out by a plane parallel to the (x, z) plane. If we fix our attention on one of the circles in the figure with constant x and look at all the circles with constant y, we see that the circles need not always meet, and if they do, they meet at any angle between 0 and π.

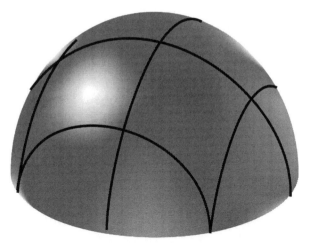

Figure 8. Circles with constant x or y coordinates on a hemisphere

Gauss had shown that if the u and v curves meet at right angles on the map, then their image curves meet at right angles on the ground if and only if $F(u, v) = 0$. Furthermore, curves that meet on the map at a certain angle have images that meet on the ground at the same angle provided also that $E(u, v) = G(u, v)$.

Such maps are said to be angle-preserving, for which the modern term is conformal. There are many of them, which is very convenient for many purposes. We shall see in the Chapter on complex functions that being angle-preserving is an important aspect of functions of a complex variable and their applications.

The curvature of surfaces

As we have already remarked, even by the beginning of the 19th century, very few results were known about surfaces. The so-called quadric surfaces had been studied—these are surfaces defined by quadratic equations, such as $x^2 + y^2 + z^2 = 4$, which describes a sphere of radius 2, and $x^2 + y^2 - z^2 = 4$, defining a surface called a hyperboloid of one sheet (see Figure 9). They are among the three-dimensional analogues of the familiar conic sections—the ellipse, parabola, and hyperbola, which are curves defined by quadratic equations, such as $x^2 + y^2 = 4$, describing a circle of radius 2, and $x^2 - y^2 = 4$, which defines a hyperbola.

Figure 9. A hyperboloid of one sheet

But few surfaces with more complicated equations had been looked at. The problem was not to produce a surface—as we have seen, that can be done in many ways—but to find things to say about it.

The decisive step in exploring the subject had been taken in 1767 by Euler, who showed how to apply calculus to the study of surfaces. He started by thinking about how mathematicians had studied curves, believing that what one wants to know about a curve in the plane was its tangent and its radius of curvature at each point. The radius of curvature of a curve at a point is the radius of the best approximating circle to the curve at that point. If we imagine traveling along the curve at unit speed, then the tangent gives us our instantaneous velocity at that point, and the radius of curvature is a measure of our acceleration. More precisely, the radius of curvature is the reciprocal of our acceleration at that point. This is familiar to drivers and their passengers: the tighter the curve, the more you feel you are turning.

Euler's idea was to study surfaces in a similar way, by looking at the curves they contain. At each point P on the surface, he considered the perpendicular to the surface at that point and looked at the planes that pass through the line (as in Figure 10). We can think of them like the pages of a book, and the perpendicular as the spine.

Figure 10. Euler slices

Each of these planes cuts the surface in a curve, and each of these curves has a radius of curvature at the given point. Here it is important to note that the curvatures of these curves can be positive or negative, depending on whether the center of curvature lies above or below the point P on the perpendicular.

For a bowl-shaped surface, such as a sphere or an ellipsoid, all the curves through a given point that are cut out in the way just described have their centers of curvature on the same side of the surface. For a saddle-shaped surface, like the one Figure 10, some of these curves have their centers of curvature on one side, and some have their centers of curvature on the other side of the surface.

Euler now kept the point (and therefore the perpendicular) fixed, varied the plane slice, and looked for the curves with the greatest and least curvature. He found that almost always at each point P, there were precisely two curves with extreme curvatures, and they were at right angles to each other. He suggested that these two curvatures be taken as the best measure of how curved the surface was at the point P.

A few years later, around 1785, a young French mathematician Jean Baptiste Meusnier came up with a simpler idea: why not look for the best approximating surface of a standard, simple kind, namely a quadric surface? This picks out Euler's curves in the surface at each point—the ones with the extreme curvatures—but in a simpler and more informative way. (We'll meet his work again in Chapter on minimal surfaces.)

Meusnier died young, fatally wounded at the Battle of Mainz in 1793, and much of the work that was done after Euler was undertaken by the French mathematician and founder of the Ecole Polytechnique in Paris, Gaspard Monge, who had originally been one of Meusnier's teachers. He picked on the result that at every point P on a surface Euler's two curves point in two perpendicular directions. If we choose one direction and follow it, we trace out a curve that always points in one of Euler's directions. In this way, we can imagine drawing a net of curves on the surface that are everywhere at right angles. Monge was interested in these curves, and what they enabled one to say about the corresponding surface.

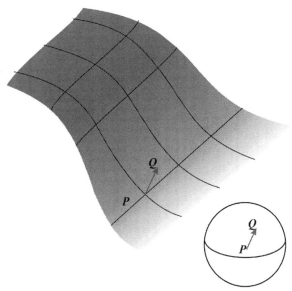

Figure 11. *The Gauss map of a surface to a sphere*

Gauss's approach, familiar to him from astronomy and surveying, was to consider a small piece of surface and suppose that at each point P there is a perpendicular PQ of unit length (see Figure 11). If we pick up a perpendicular and move it, without changing its direction, until its base point P is at a fixed point O, then its end point Q has moved and now lies at a point Q' on the unit sphere centre O. If we do this for every perpendicular in a region of the surface, then the corresponding end points lie on a region of the unit sphere, and in this way, we have constructed a map from the original piece of surface to the sphere. More intuitively, we can think of each perpendicular as pointing at a point of the celestial sphere and regard that sphere as a sphere of unit radius.

Let us see what the map does if we move the point P along a curve in our piece of surface. If the curve is only slightly curved, then the perpendiculars vary little from point to point, and the corresponding curve on the sphere is mapped to a small curve on the unit sphere. But if the curve on the surface is tightly curved, then the perpendiculars vary greatly along that curve, and the curve on the surface is mapped to a large curve on the unit sphere.

Rather surprisingly, perhaps, if the curve is a straight line on a cylinder, then the perpendiculars vary not at all from point to point, and the straight line is mapped to a single point on the unit sphere. Let us set such cases aside.

If we move our base point along one of Euler's curves, then the perpendiculars all lie in the same plane, and so their images under the map lie on an arc of a great circle on the sphere. So, if we take a region of the surface and shade in lots of the two families of Euler curves that pass through it, the image of that region is made up of lots of great circles in two families, one meeting the other at right angles.

Gauss discovered that there was an important connection between the area of a region of the surface and the area of the corresponding region on the sphere. To be precise, consider a region S that contains the point P, and suppose that the region S shrinks down until it consists only of the point P. Let S' be the region on the sphere that corresponds to the region S, then it too shrinks down to the point P' that is the image of P. Gauss found that as the regions shrank to their corresponding points the ratio of the areas

$$\text{area of } S' : \text{area of } S$$

tended to a limit, and that this limiting value was the reciprocal of the product of the radii of curvature of Euler's curves. He proposed to take this number as the measure of the curvature of the surface at P.

Why was this a remarkable thing to do? After all, as a number, it is simply the product of two numbers already known to be important. The answer is that this number is intrinsic: it is determined by measurements that can be taken in the surface alone and do not depend on how the surface is embedded in space. This insight is the start of a story that leads directly to Riemann and then, half a century later, to Einstein's theory of gravity.

As already mentioned, Gauss had shown that the expression for a very small distance ds on a surface in terms of the coordinates of nearby points is:

$$ds^2 = E(u,v)du^2 + 2F(u,v)dudv + G(u,v)dv^2.$$

Gauss now calculated the expression for the curvature of a surface at a point. He gave a very general form of the answer, which is long and intimidating, but it showed something extraordinary: it involves the functions E, F, and G, and their derivatives with respect to u and v—but it does not involve the functions x, y, and z. This means it is independent of the way the surface is depicted in space, and can be determined entirely from a knowledge of E, F, and G.

Gauss's analysis of curvature means that some properties of a surface, such as its curvature, can be determined directly from the metric. It means that if you have only the functions E, F, and G you can still talk about a surface and those of its properties that are intrinsic to it. These properties include:

- the lengths of curves in a surface,
- the curves lying in a surface that are of shortest length joining two points on a surface, and
- the angle between two intersecting curves in the surface.

In particular, Gauss showed that you can only map a piece of one surface onto another without altering the distances between points if the two pieces of surface have the same curvature at corresponding points. He thought this was so remarkable that he called this theorem the "Theorema egregium" or "exceptional theorem." For example, a cylinder and a plane both have the same curvature everywhere (zero, in fact), and so what is on the cylinder can be copied exactly onto the plane—which is how old-fashioned printing was done. Another consequence is a second proof of Euler's result that there is no distance-preserving map of a sphere (or the surface of the Earth) onto a plane. This fact that had surely been known to cartographers for centuries. Gauss stated the point this way (Gauss, Anzeige 1827, in *Werke* IV, 344, transl. repr. (Dombrowski 1979, 89-91)):

> These theorems lead to the consideration of the theory of curved surfaces from a new point of view, where a rich and still wholly uncultivated field is open to investigation.
> If we consider surfaces not as boundaries of bodies, but as bodies of which one dimension vanishes, and if at the same time we conceive them as flexible but not extensible, we see that two essentially different relations must be distinguished, namely, on the one hand, those that presuppose a definite form of the surface in space; on the other hand, those that are independent of the various forms which the surface may assume. This discussion is concerned with the latter. In accordance with what has been said, the measure of curvature belongs to this case. But it is easily seen that the consideration of figures constructed upon the surface, their angles, their areas and their integral curvatures, the joining of the points by means of shortest lines, and the like, also belong to this case. All such investigations must start from this, that the very nature of the curved surface is given by means of the expression of any linear element in the form
> $$ds = \sqrt{(E(u,v)du^2 + 2F(u,v)dudv + G(u,v)dv^2)}.$$

To proceed further, we have to turn to a mathematical scandal of the 1820s, which Gauss called the "shameful part" of geometry—whether Euclidean geometry is the only possible geometry that can be an accurate description of physical space.

Non-Euclidean geometry

Euclid's *Elements* had set the standard for rigor in mathematics in every culture that came across it over the two millennia since it was written. Arab and more generally Islamic mathematicians took it to heart, as did later mathematicians in the West. In the 18th century, it was the basis of geometry at every level, from simple school education to research, however, diluted for pedagogic purposes and mixed with algebra for advanced work. But in all those years, there were a few critical voices who disputed the quality, although not necessarily the truth, of the *Elements*.

The greatest source of complaints was Euclid's account of parallel lines, the so-called parallel postulate. He had asserted that if two coplanar lines l and m cross a third n and the angles α and β are such that

$$\alpha + \beta < \pi$$

then the lines l and m meet and indeed meet on the side of the line n where the angles are.

This is easier to understand if the equivalent statement is made that: if l is a line and P is a point, then every line through P that lies in the plane of P and l meets the line l except one, which is the unique parallel to l through P.

Mathematicians seem to have objected, arguing that this claim was not obviously true, unlike most, if not all, of Euclid's other basic assumptions. But the parallel postulate was essential—almost all the major results in the *Elements* depend on it, notably the Pythagorean theorem. So, numerous mathematicians—including the astronomer Ptolemy, as well as Arab, Islamic, and Western mathematicians—set out to prove the postulate using just the other, intuitively acceptable, postulates. All these attempts failed.

Gauss, however, was skeptical. He published refutations of some of these attempts, including one provided by a college friend Farkas Bolyai. But he found himself drawn into controversies that he did not enjoy, so he finally withdrew. Then in 1818, a law professor called F.K. Schweikart sent him something rather different, a description of some theorems that would be true if the parallel postulate was false.

How could the postulate be false? One way would be if every two lines met, and no lines were parallel. But this hypothesis is provably inconsistent with the other assumptions Euclid had made, in particular, the assumption that any line segment can be extended indefinitely. The other way would be that if l is a line and P is a point not on l, then there are infinitely many lines through P that lie in the plane of P and l and do not meet the line l. In this case, parallels to l through P exist but are not unique.

It was already known that, in this case, figures in geometry have unexpected properties. For example, if two triangles have their corresponding angles equal in pairs, then they have the same size. This is not true in Euclidean geometry, where one triangle can be an exact scale copy of another. Also, in the new geometry, the angle sum of a triangle is always less than π. Indeed, as Lambert knew, the difference between π and the angle sum of a triangle was proportional to the area of the triangle.

These results and more had been discovered by people hoping to nudge them into a contradiction with Euclid's other assumptions, but despite many false alarms, all had failed. Schweikart had not found a new result—his novelty was in accepting it. Now he wanted to know if no less a figure than Gauss agreed with him.

Indeed, he did. In typical fashion, Gauss wrote back to say he knew all this and more. He even said that he could derive all the results in this new plane geometry. How Schweikart reacted to this lofty display of Gauss's brilliance is unknown. He did, however, have a nephew who shortly afterwards wrote a long muddle-headed book arguing that the new geometry was false and Euclid's therefore true. He too asked Gauss for an opinion, but Gauss wisely refused to offer one.

Most likely, Gauss knew a lot about the new geometry. He seems to have known the trigonometrical formulae appropriate to it and to have decided that on those grounds there were two logically possible geometries: Euclid's and the new one. He drew the important conclusion that the truth of geometry was no longer a matter to be settled *a priori*, like arithmetic, but was an empirical question.

Figure 12. Nikolai Ivanovich Lobachevsky (1792-1856)

Everything should have changed in the years between 1829 and 1831, when János Bolyai (the son of Farkas) in Romania-Hungary and Nikolai Ivanovich Lobachevsky in Kazan, Russia, published independent accounts of the new geometry. Bolyai published his account as an Appendix to his father's two-volume account of geometry written in Latin; not the best way to get it noticed. But besides two lengthy accounts in Russian, Lobachevsky published others in French and German.

Bolyai and Lobachevsky agreed on almost every aspect of the implications of the assumption that parallels exist but are not unique; even their methods, which were trigonometrical, were largely the same. They also surpassed Gauss by being the first to give a detailed examination of the three-dimensional version of the new geometry.

This was essential if their claim that the new geometry might be true, and physical space was to be described by it and not by Euclid, had any chance of success. Unfortunately for both men, the world's response was malign neglect.

Gauss gave their work a tepid welcome. He wrote to Farkas Bolyai, who had sent him a copy of what he and his son had done, to say that he was unable to praise his son's work "because to do so would be to praise myself"; and went on, once again, to claim that he knew it all already. In fact, there is little evidence that Gauss had explored the three-dimensional geometry adequately, although it is clear that he did already believe it could be true. János Bolyai was so offended that he never published again.

As for Lobachevsky, Gauss nominated him as a member of the Göttingen Academy of Sciences, a nice honor to have but one that provided no defense against the two reviews Lobachevsky's work received, including an especially harsh one by Mikhail Ostrogradsky, a well-established mathematician in Moscow who rubbished Lobachevsky's Russian accounts of his discoveries.

Had Gauss come to the aid of Bolyai and Lobachevsky by publicly endorsing their work and contributing to it, they would surely not have gone to their graves unacknowledged and almost forgotten. Why Gauss held back is not known. One reason may well be that although Gauss had developed the magnificent theory of curvature described above, it was not until the 1840s that he thought to see how the new geometry fitted in. It then became clear that it is the geometry on a surface of constant negative curvature.

This is initially consoling: there is a surface to which it applies, just as spherical geometry applies to a sphere. But then doubt can set in. All that the theory of curvature does is provide small pieces of a surface of constant negative curvature. Can we be sure that these pieces can be extended indefinitely and capture all two-dimensional non-Euclidean space? Can we draw on it figures of any size we like? Do the pieces perhaps fit together in unexpected ways, or even come to a halt? Gauss had no answer to such questions, and we shall see why below.

Another partial answer is that Gauss had not extended his theory of surfaces to a theory of three-dimensional objects, and so he was in no position to discuss it from that point of view. He could not formulate a precise concept of three-dimensional curvature.

But Gauss disliked controversy. He may well have felt that it was for Bolyai and Lobachevsky to promote their own discoveries and refute all the objections. By doing so, he left the way open for Riemann.

Dirichlet

Figure 13. *Peter Gustav Lejeune Dirichlet (1805-1859)*

Among the German mathematicians drawn to mathematics after Gauss, Peter Gustav Lejeune Dirichlet stands out. He had been born in Düren near Cologne in 1805, which was French territory at the time, and when he found that no adequate training in mathematics was available locally, he went to Paris, then the undisputed center of the mathematical world. His contacts helped him to get to know Joseph Fourier, whose work on the representation of functions as infinite sums of sines and cosines (Fourier series, we call them today) was finally attracting the recognition it deserved. Fourier paid scant attention to the convergence of his series, belonging as he did to the last generation for whom formal criteria were enough; however, one of Dirichlet's first major works, *On the Convergence of*

Trigonometric Series that Serve to Represent an Arbitrary Function Between Given Limits, published in 1829, showed that well-behaved functions have convergent Fourier series and agree with the function defined by the Fourier series (as we shall see in Chapter on real analysis). A function defined on an interval $[a, b]$ (i.e., all the numbers $a \leq x \leq b$) is well-behaved if it is continuous, and is either always increasing or always decreasing. The same is true for functions that are made up of finitely many such functions (if there is a jump from one piece to the next, the Fourier series takes the average of the values on either side of the jump).

Riemann learned about Dirichlet's interest in the theory of Fourier series, as we shall see in Chapter 7, and he wrote a strikingly informative history of the topic.

By then, Dirichlet had become known by solving a case of Fermat's Last Theorem. This is the claim that there are no solutions in positive integers $x, y, z, n > 2$ of the equation

$$x^n + y^n = z^n.$$

Fermat had already proved that there are no solutions when $n = 4$ and, a few over-confident assertions aside, Euler had dealt with the case $n = 3$. In 1826 Dirichlet, who had just turned 21, did most of the case of $n = 5$, leaving the French number theorist Legendre to finish one troublesome special case. Legendre was able to do the work, but for whatever reason, perhaps his advanced age (he was 73), he omitted Dirichlet's name from the resulting publication!

On his return to Germany, Dirichlet became a Professor at the newly established University of Berlin. His connections, along with his ability at the piano, now gave him entry to the Mendelssohn family, and he eventually married the composer Felix Mendelssohn Bartholdy's sister Rebecka. He continued to develop as a number theorist, and in 1837 he discovered the remarkable result that every arithmetic progression

$$a, a + b, a + 2b, \ldots, a + kb, \ldots$$

where a and b are integers whose only common divisor is 1, contains infinitely many primes (Dirichlet 1837). For example, the sequence defined by $a = 5, b = 6$ begins 5, 11, 17, 23, 29, all of which are prime; Dirichlet's theorem says that the sequence contains infinitely many more primes.

Dirichlet also understood better than anyone else at the time the need for high standards of rigor in mathematics, which is a subject where delicate results cannot be found without considerable experience and cannot be proved easily or by confident assertion. This was an issue that Gauss also promoted, and Riemann too, although not all the time, as we shall see.

Contemporaries and rivals

In Göttingen, Riemann also acquired an important friend: Richard Dedekind. Dedekind was primarily interested in algebra and number theory, publishing much of his best works as additional chapters to Dirichlet's *Lectures* on Gauss's number theory. But he valued what he saw as Riemann's conceptual approach to mathematics, preferring it to the heavy computational style of many other mathematicians of the day.

Dedekind was five years younger than Riemann, more socially adept and better connected; being a good pianist, he also became acquainted through Dirichlet with the Mendelssohn family in Berlin. And, eventually, he was to be Riemann's obituarist (Dedekind 1876) and one of the two editors of Riemann's *Collected Works*.

Other people also helped the young Riemann: Oscar Schlömilch, a textbook writer and journal editor; Gustav Durège, a former colleague who became a professor in Prague; and the mathematician Gustav Roch, a former student of Riemann's, all helped to get Riemann's ideas published.

But once Riemann began to publish, he had rivals, and after his death in 1866, they moved steadily to dominate the subject using very different methods of their own. By the 1850s, the University of Berlin was headed by the trio of mathematicians who could in different ways claim to be the best in their field: the number theorists Ernst Eduard Kummer and his former student Leopold Kronecker, and the analyst and relatively new arrival Karl Weierstrass, who was in his 40s when he began to publish.

Of these, it was Weierstrass whose interests most overlapped with Riemann's, but while Riemann was a geometer, Weierstrass was an algebraist who laid great store on rigor and increasingly distrusted geometrical arguments. They were fine as a path to discovery, he conceded, but not as proof what intuition might, not always correctly, suggest. While Weierstrass was critical but appreciative, his former student Hermann Amandus Schwarz was simply aggressive. Much of his work in the years after Riemann's death was devoted to deriving—by Weierstrassian methods—results that Riemann had first claimed. It was as if, in that way, he took possession of them. After all, every mathematician knows that in the end, the only results that count are the ones that have been proved.

2. Geometry

I n the mid-1850s, Riemann extended the study of the differential geometry of surfaces to embrace spaces of any number of dimensions. His concept of higher-dimensional spaces became known as Riemannian geometry and laid the foundations for the development of Einstein's theory of general relativity half a century later.

As was required, Riemann presented his ideas in a lecture he delivered to the Philosophy Faculty of Göttingen University on June 10, 1854. It is entitled "On the Hypotheses Which Lie at the Foundations of Geometry," and was published posthumously in 1867. To this day it remains one of the most important works in modern geometry.

Riemann's n-dimensional geometries

As we have seen, Gauss was clear that a surface is given when we have its description in coordinates. For the plane, these coordinates are usually its (x, y) coordinates, where the x-axis may be the East-West axis and the y-axis the North-South axis. For the sphere, the coordinates are usually longitude and latitude. We sometimes forget about the difference between the point on the surface and the point on the plane that represents the point on the surface. When we say that Greenwich has longitude zero and latitude $51°48'$ N we may mean either the place or the point on a page of an atlas with coordinates $(0, 51°48')$. But when necessary we do distinguish, and we speak of the point with grid reference such-and-such.

Mathematicians do this when they talk about surfaces, and so shall we. For a general surface, we shall use (u, v) coordinates in the plane but measure distances between points by using the formula for distances that Gauss obtained (the metric):

$$ds^2 = E(u,v)du^2 + 2F(u,v)dudv + G(u,v)dv^2.$$

Now every point on the surface has coordinates (u,v) and certain properties of curves and other figures on the surface can be understood, without specifying how the surface lies in three-dimensional space, which we denote by $\mathbb{R}^3$.

In fact, this is not quite the same thing as saying that the surface need not be taken to lie in $\mathbb{R}^3$ at all. Gauss had begun his analysis by supposing that there are three functions $x(u,v)$, $y(u,v)$, and $z(u,v)$ that map a piece of the (u,v) plane into $\mathbb{R}^3$, and concluded by showing that many properties of a surface depend only on the metric. That is, they depend on $E(u,v)$, $F(u,v)$, and $G(u,v)$ (and their derivatives with respect to u and v) but not on the x, y, and z. Still, one might hope that given E, F, and G there are corresponding functions x, y, and z that give rise to E, F, and G, and so the surface "really" does lie in $\mathbb{R}^3$.

It is not clear what Gauss thought about this question, but we know what Riemann did. He separated geometry into two parts: an intrinsic part that studies properties that depend only on the metric, and an extrinsic part that studies how the surface lies in $\mathbb{R}^3$.

More precisely—and this surely is what impressed Gauss—Riemann did the same thing but in any number of dimensions. It was an enormous extension of geometry, beyond anything Gauss or anyone else had ever contemplated.

What does it mean to talk of a space of n dimensions? In Riemann's view, each point of the space is specified when n numbers are given that collectively determine its position with respect to some system of coordinates. We are familiar with this in two dimensions—points in a plane—and in three points in space. We also know of surfaces in space whose points are specified by two numbers, for example, latitude and longitude on a sphere. One could say that all Riemann did was to see no reason to stop at three, and allow any number of coordinates.

Then Riemann had to specify a metric on an n-dimensional space. He took Gauss's expression

$$ds^2 = E(u,v)du^2 + 2F(u,v)dudv + G(u,v)dv^2$$

and generalized it in the obvious way, so that in terms of coordinates $u_1, u_2, \ldots, u_n$ the metric takes the form

$$ds^2 = g_{11}du_1^2 + 2g_{12}du_1du_2 + \cdots g_{nn}du_n^2.$$

The g_{jk} are functions of $u_1, u_2, \ldots, u_n$ and when $n = 2$ we have

$$g_{11} = E, \quad g_{12} = F, \quad g_{22} = G.$$

The only condition that the functions must satisfy is that the distances between points are always real and never negative, and so the above expression for ds^2 has to be always positive. In the case of surfaces, this implies that $EG - F^2$ must always be positive, which still leaves us with lots of possibilities for a metric.

Riemann then talked about curves in an n-dimensional space, the angles where they cross, and similar geometrical features. But what about intrinsic curvature in n dimensions? This has to be some expression in the g_{jk} and their derivatives with respect to the coordinates $u_1, u_2, \ldots, u_n$. How can it be understood?

The simplest idea is to pick a point P^0 in the space, which we may suppose has coordinates $(u_1^0, u_2^0, \ldots, u_n^0)$ and to look at the nearby points where only two of the coordinates have varied, say u_j and u_k. These points form a piece of a surface, because they depend on only two numbers. The variation in the other coordinates is zero because they are held constant, and so the only dus that vary are du_j and du_k, all the others vanish. The metric therefore takes the form

$$g_{jj}du_j^2 + 2g_jg_kdu_jdu_k + g_{kk}du_k^2.$$

This is the metric on the surface under consideration, and it has an intrinsic curvature. It is called a sectional curvature of the n-dimensional space.

There are n choices for the first coordinate to be allowed to vary, and $n - 1$ for the next, but the order of these choices does not matter, so there are $\frac{1}{2}n(n - 1)$ choices to be made of surfaces through the point P^0. There are, of course, infinitely many surfaces that pass through P^0, just as there are infinitely many curves in the plane that pass through the origin. But in the plane, every direction through the origin is a linear combination of two (usually taken to be defined by the standard x and y axes). In the same way, the surfaces picked out above are enough to allow a mathematician to form a clear picture of how an n-dimensional space is curved on it at any given point.

Novel or not, all this might sound like the kind of thing a mathematician might do. The important question is: why isn't it just an example of taking something useful—the geometry of Euclidean, physical space—and making it into an abstract game with a useless extension to any number of coordinates?

Set "useless" aside for a minute. The idea is that there are geometries in any number of dimensions, and there are many geometries in any dimension greater than 1. Specify a metric, and you have a geometry in which you can talk about lengths and angles. Now, almost anybody would say that geometry is about figures (curves, shapes, whatever), and their defining sizes, lengths, angles, and so forth. It takes an elaborate mathematical culture to say that geometry is what is talked about in Euclid's *Elements*, with its undefined (or, perhaps, badly defined) terms like straight line and angle, and its array of postulates. Riemann restarted geometry where anyone naturally would, with a way to talk about lengths and angles.

Let us now consider the case where the dimension is $n = 3$. The Euclidean case has the metric

$$ds^2 = du_1^2 + du_2^2 + du_3^2,$$

where $g_{11} = g_{22} = g_{33} = 1$ and all the g_{jk} with $j \neq k$ vanish. Plainly, there are infinitely many different metrics, but perhaps they could all reduce to this one by changing coordinates. However, they cannot reduce to this one unless they have the same sectional curvatures at every point as Euclidean three-dimensional space does (which are all zero), because sectional curvature is intrinsic and therefore independent of the choice of coordinates. So, that there are many surfaces with non-zero curvature implies that there are many three-dimensional spaces that cannot be Euclidean space.

Riemann's starting point for an analysis of geometry was not only more natural than Euclid's, but it also led immediately to the conclusion that the three-dimensional space we inhabit need not be Euclidean! Whether it is Euclidean or has a different geometry, as Bolyai and Lobachevsky had speculated, is a fact that can only be determined empirically.

But what about the "useless" extension to any number of coordinates that we referred to above? Is n-dimensional space merely a playground for mathematicians performing unneeded work? In the opinion of many Riemann contemporaries, the answer was both yes and no. Yes, because the technical complexities of n-dimensional geometry drove most mathematicians away, and those who tackled it did so as a formal exercise with scarcely an application in sight. No, because there were already many situations where more than three coordinates are required; the intractable three-body problem in celestial mechanics is one such example, as we shall see shortly. New mathematics is always hard but geometrical language can help, so gradually Riemann's ideas gained support.

But did Riemann know of the work of Bolyai and Lobachevsky? Was his work driven by an attempt to make sense of the new geometry that these two mathematicians had proclaimed? It could have been. Gauss might have told him about it. Or Riemann could have read Lobachevsky's article in a journal we know he borrowed from the Göttingen University library. But it seems that the answer was No.

In the published version of the lecture that Riemann gave as part of the examination that so impressed Gauss, Riemann began with some critical remarks about how geometry was currently studied. He said that it "takes for granted the notion of space" as well as the first principles of constructions in space. Its basic concepts have only nominal definitions, he observed, so it is not clear what they are about. (What, after all, does it mean to say, as Euclid's *Elements* does, that a straight line lies evenly upon itself? The "definition" only makes sense if you already know what a straight line is.) Crucial properties are determined from axioms, Riemann explained, but this leaves the relationships between the axioms obscure to the point where it is not even clear a priori if the relationships are mutually consistent.

As we have seen, Riemann's remedy was not a list of new, better, axioms. Instead, he cited the work of Legendre as indicative of the poverty of even recent work, plainly because he thought the whole axiomatic attempt to give a geometrical account of physical space was misguided. And in unpublished notes from the early 1850s, he called such enquiries "extremely unfruitful" which, as Erhard Scholz argued (Scholz 1982a, 218), makes it very unlikely that Riemann had seen any of Lobachevsky's work, which starts with a new axiom about lines.

It is therefore clear that Riemann's starting point was a desire to grasp the essence of Gauss's idea of intrinsic geometry and to generalize it to spaces of any number of dimensions. He also acknowledged some of the ideas of the philosopher Johann Friedrich Herbart, whose most important book was *Psychology as Science Newly Founded on Experience, Metaphysics and Mathematics*. In his private notes, Riemann wrote that he agreed with Herbart's ideas about psychology and epistemology, but not about ontology. Nor did he support Herbart's ideas about space, time, and motion, and particularly those about intelligible space, which Herbart had presented as a mental construct that makes the explanation of matter possible.

Riemann took from Herbart the idea that there are varying quantities and objects that are made up of several varying quantities, such as space and geometry, although he dropped Herbart's restriction that space was three-dimensional. He disagreed with Herbart's account of how our ideas of space are generated from experience, and instead advocated seeing mathematics as coherent systems of concepts that could be matched against the coherence of the natural world. The elucidation of fundamental concepts is characteristic of Riemann's work in every topic he touched, and it is the single most defining feature of modern mathematics.

Riemann's lecture was given not just before Gauss but, at least in principle, in front of the Philosophy Faculty, which included the Mathematics Department, implying that philosophers would be present. For us, this is a mixed blessing, because we have verbal expressions where, at least to a mathematician, some formulae would help. But there is one happy exception, and that concerns Riemann's account of spaces of constant curvature.

Euclidean space is an example: in any number of dimensions, it has zero curvature everywhere. Among two-dimensional spaces, the sphere is an example of a space with constant positive curvature. Indeed, if the sphere has radius R its curvature is $1/R^2$ at every point. Riemann presumably felt that the simplest non-trivial examples of n-dimensional spaces were those of constant curvature.

Riemann wrote down the metric for a space of constant negative curvature, and we can easily see how this can be obtained, at least for surfaces.

We start by writing a formula for the metric on a sphere using a map that represents the sphere on a plane. The map we shall use is called stereographic projection (see Figure) 14, and it has a long history in cartography. It associates to a point P on the sphere the point P' in the tangent plane at the North Pole that lies on the straight line, joining the South Pole to P. (There is no image for the South Pole itself.)

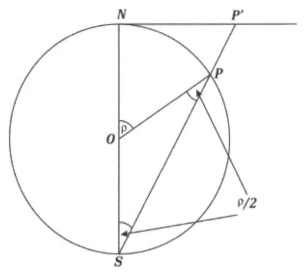

Figure 14. Chasing angles

The merit of this map is that it maps angles on the sphere to equal angles on the plane, as we shall see shortly. This makes it useful for giving an idea of the shapes of regions on the sphere, but once again the map distorts distances unevenly. Distances near N, the North Pole, are not altered much, while distances near the South Pole S are greatly stretched.

Let us examine how this stretching varies from point to point. We consider the arc of a great circle from N to P of length ρ, where R is the radius of the sphere, and purely for convenience, we take $R = \frac{1}{2}$. What happens to the arc under stereographic projection?

From the figure we see that the arc NP subtends an angle of ρ at O, the center of the sphere, and so the angle NSP is $\rho/2$. The length NS is 1, so the length NP' is $r = \tan \frac{\rho}{2}$.

Therefore

$$dr = \frac{1}{2} \sec^2 \frac{\rho}{2} d\rho.$$

But we also have the trigonometric formula $\sec^2 \rho = 1 + \tan^2 \rho$, which in the present case gives us that

$$dr = \frac{1}{2}(1 + r^2)d\rho,$$

and tidying this up, we get

$$\frac{2}{1 + r^2}dr = d\rho.$$

This formula says that equal steps of $d\rho$ on the geodesic arc from N to P correspond to larger and larger steps of dr on the plane, because, as r increases, the fraction $\frac{2}{1+r^2}$ decreases.

We can write down the formula that relates the metric on the sphere to the metric on the plane via stereographic projection (see the Section More about the Mathematics at the end of this chapter). It is

$$ds^2 = \left(\frac{2}{1 + r^2}\right)^2 (dr^2 + r^2 d\theta^2).$$

This gives lengths ds on the sphere in terms of quantities we can measure on the plane $(r, dr, \theta, d\theta)$. Notice that this formula reduces to the earlier formula for radial distances in the plane, when θ is constant and so $d\theta = 0$.

But what if we started with the formula? What if we were given a set of points in the plane (in our case, the entire plane) and the distance formula above—what could we do?

Riemann's answer was that we could certainly do geometry. We can talk about the distances between nearby points and the distances along curves by adding up all the distances between nearby points on the curve. Adding up lots of infinitesimally small distances is done by integration, so along straight lines out of N in the plane we have

$$\int_0^\rho ds = \int_0^r \frac{2}{1 + t^2}dt.$$

This works out to give $\tan \frac{\rho}{2} = r$ (see the next Box). This is the result we started out with when we were looking at stereographic projection. Now we can say that from the formula alone, we are likely to be looking in the plane at a map of the sphere, indeed one given by stereographic projection.

The length integral

The integral on the left-hand side is simply ρ. On the right-hand side, we set $t = \tan\frac{\rho}{2}$, so

$$dt = \frac{1}{2}\sec^2\frac{\rho}{2}d\rho = \frac{1}{2}\left(1 + \tan^2\frac{\rho}{2}\right),$$

and the integral becomes $\int_0^{t=r} d\rho$, which is the value of ρ when $t = r$. What is this value? Well, we set $t = \tan\frac{\rho}{2}$, so $\rho = 2\arctan t$, and so when $t = r$ we have $\frac{\rho}{2} = \arctan t$ and $\tan\frac{\rho}{2} = r$

Certainly, with this formula we can talk about the shortest curve between two given points, we can talk about circles (the collection of points that are all a given distance from a given point), and many other geometric features of what is depicted in the plane.

But could we discover that we were talking about the usual geometry on a sphere (strictly speaking, the sphere with a point removed)? Almost. Riemann's theory shows that there is a concept of curvature associated with our two-dimensional set of points and its novel definition of distance. In the case at hand, this curvature turns out to be the positive constant $1/R^2$, and the curvature, in Riemann's sense, of a sphere of radius R is $1/R^2$. So, either there are several surfaces of constant positive curvature, of which the sphere is one, or there is only one surface of constant positive curvature, and the sphere is it. It's quite a tricky matter to show that the second alternative is the correct one, and so we could discover from the map that we have been talking about geometry on a sphere (or pieces of a sphere) all along. This makes explicit how we might obtain from a map of a surface a good geometric grasp of what the surface is itself.

How did this help Riemann to find altogether novel geometries? He did a simple but profound thing. He wrote down the metric that is obtained by a simple change of sign:

$$ds^2 = \left(\frac{2}{1-r^2}\right)^2 (dr^2 + r^2 d\theta^2).$$

As before, if we regard θ as a constant, therefore $d\theta = 0$, simplifying the formula to

$$ds = \frac{1}{1-r^2} dr.$$

For this to make sense, the right-hand side must be positive, and so we must have $-1 < r < 1$. But otherwise, we have a geometry to talk about. It is a new geometry defined on the set of points (r, θ) in the disc of radius 1, so $r < 1$. This time, integration gives us that

$$S = \int_0^S ds = \int_0^R \frac{dr}{1-r^2} = \tanh^{-1} R,$$

so

$$R = \tanh S.$$

Hyperbolic functions

In the 1740s, Euler had deduced from the infinite series

$$\sin x = x - \frac{x^3}{3!} + \frac{x^5}{5!} - \frac{x^7}{7!} + \cdots$$

$$\cos x = 1 - \frac{x^2}{2!} + \frac{x^4}{4!} - \frac{x^6}{6!} + \cdots$$

and

$$e^x = 1 + x + \frac{x^2}{2!} + \frac{x^3}{3!} + \frac{x^4}{4!} + \cdots$$

that

$$\sin x = \frac{e^{ix} - e^{-ix}}{2i} \quad \text{and} \quad \cos x = \frac{e^{ix} + e^{-ix}}{2}.$$

Because $\sin^2 x + \cos^2 x = 1$ these functions are often used in studies of circles and ellipses.

The hyperbolic functions are close relatives of these functions. They are defined as follows:

$$\sinh x = \frac{e^x - e^{-x}}{2}, \quad \cosh x = \frac{e^x + e^{-x}}{2}, \text{and} \quad \tanh x = \frac{\sinh x}{\cosh x}.$$

It is clear that $-1 < \tanh x < 1$ for all values of x.

The "hyperbolic" part of their name derives from the fact that $\cosh^2 t - \sinh^2 t = 1$,
so the hyperbola $x^2 - y^2 = 1$ is parameterized by $(\cosh t, \sinh t)$; these functions are often used in studies of hyperbolas.

Can we say what this new geometry is? Well, the calculation of curvature can be carried out as before, and it shows that the curvature of the new space is constant and negative. Riemann left the story at that. But a young Italian mathematician Eugenio Beltrami did more. Beltrami knew three things that Riemann could have known, but if he did, he did not mention them. One is that there are surfaces in space of constant negative curvature (see the next Box). The second is that the angle sum of a triangle drawn on such a surface, whose sides are curves of shortest length joining their endpoints, is always less than π. The third is that in non-Euclidean geometry, the angle sum of a triangle is always less than π.

A surface of constant negative curvature

The surface is obtained by rotating a curve about an axis. The curve is obtained as the answer to the following problem: a heavy object is placed at the point $(a, 0)$ and is attached to a man at the origin. The man now walks along the positive y axis pulling the object behind him. What is the path of the heavy object?

If you prefer a more prosaic account, consider this: what is the curve with the property that at every point P on the curve the length of the tangent to the curve between P and the axis is constant and equal to a?

The solution curve is known as the tractrix—we get the word "tractor" from the same association with pulling or dragging.

Unfortunately, the curve has a truly uninformative equation, but it can be parametrised usefully:
$$x(t) = a\,sech\,t, \quad y(t) = a(t - \tanh t)$$
(the function $sech\,t = \frac{1}{\cosh t}$.)

It was discovered in the 1830s that if this curve is rotated around its axis, it generates a surface of constant negative curvature $\frac{-1}{a^2}$, sometimes called a pseudosphere (see Figure 15).

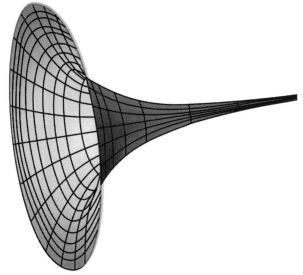

Figure 15. A pseudosphere

There is a very fine sculpture of this surface in the sculpture park at Chateau La Coste near Aix-en-Provence in France.

Why does this not settle the question of the existence of non-Euclidean geometry? Because these surfaces are like cylinders—there are closed curves on them that cannot be shrunk to a point. The aim all along was to construct a geometry that could be a geometry of space, and such surfaces are implausible on physical grounds.

To show that a non-Euclidean geometry was possible, Beltrami needed a surface with no strange curves. To obtain one, he started from the metric that arises from geodetic projection of a hemisphere on a plane, and changed the sign of one term in it. This map associates to a point P on the Northern Hemisphere the point P' on the tangent plane to the North Pole that lies on the line OPP', where O is the center of the hemisphere. This altered the image from being the whole plane to the interior of a disc, altering the curvature from constant positive to constant negative. Under geodetic projection, curves of shortest length on the sphere map to straight lines in the image. In the altered map, straight lines are still images of curves of shortest length in the original. Angles can be defined in the disc, although like distances, they appear distorted in the map. When this is done, it turns out that the angle sum of any triangle is less than π. It is easy to draw two lines in the disc that do not meet (what happens outside the disc doesn't count—the geometry is entirely about what happens inside the disc). So the disc, with the new metric, is a model of non-Euclidean geometry.

It is tempting to think of the disc as a picture of some original surface. But what is the original?

Part of the insight that Riemann had, and that Beltrami came to appreciate, is that the image tells you all you need to know about a surface of constant negative curvature. There does not need to be a surface in physical space that corresponds to it. In fact, as it turned out, there is no such surface in physical space. Large pieces of it can be drawn, but not the whole thing. Riemann was the first to see that there are two questions to be asked about non-Euclidean geometry. The first asks: "Is there a surface of constant negative curvature in which curves of shortest length have all the properties of straight lines in Euclidean geometry except the parallel postulate?" The second one asks: "Is this surface a surface in Euclidean space, with the metric induced from Euclidean space?" The first question is answered affirmatively, and that shows that non-Euclidean geometry makes coherent sense. The second question is answered negatively, but that does not mean that non-Euclidean geometry does not exist; it simply means that we cannot draw pictures of it the way we can draw pictures of geometry on a surface of constant positive curvature.

Immediate consequences

Riemann's ideas about geometry were difficult for other mathematicians to understand. The leading English mathematician, Arthur Cayley, never fully accepted them. Even those who recognized that geometry was about spaces (sets of points) with a metric, found it hard to shake off the idea that Euclidean geometry was the "real" thing. It was, after all, the simplest model of the space of their daily lives. There seemed to be no reason for anyone interested in applying mathematics to use a new geometry, nor did new geometrical ideas seem to have any connection to the other, purer, parts of mathematics. If all that it promised was complicated calculations, then why do it?

In fact, one reason was mechanics—the study of moving objects. At the beginning of the 19th century, the French mathematician Pierre-Simon Laplace had successfully resolved much of the subtle behavior of the planets and their satellites; as a result, the Newtonian theory of gravity had become completely accepted. The difficult problems that he solved were mostly three-body problems: the motion of three bodies under their mutual gravitational attractions.

For example, as Jupiter and Saturn orbit the Sun they are at times far apart and at times less so. When they are far apart, at opposite points in their orbits, they appear widely separated in the sky, and may not be both visible at once. But when they are at roughly the same points in their orbits, they appear close together in the sky.

Jupiter's orbit is closer to the Sun, so it travels faster than Saturn. As the two planets approach each other, the gravitational pull of Jupiter, which is more massive than Saturn, slows Saturn down. Then, as Jupiter overtakes Saturn and moves away, Saturn is pulled along for a while, and speeds up. These departures from the motion that would occur if the planets did not attract each other but felt only the force of the Sun were well-known to astronomers, and Laplace was able to show that Newtonian theory could explain them.

The three bodies in this problem are the Sun, Jupiter, and Saturn. They can be thought of as points for the purposes of discussing their orbits, but each point needs three coordinates to be located in space. Moreover, Newton's laws of motion are about bodies, the forces between them, and their accelerations, so the velocities of the bodies must be treated as coordinates as well before the motion can be described properly. Putting all this together results in nine coordinates for positions and nine more for velocities, for a total of 18 coordinates. A mathematician would say that the three-body problem involved 18 variables, and if he or she was geometrically minded, that it took place in an 18-dimensional space.

Things aren't quite that bad. For many purposes, one can assume that the motion takes place in a plane (Jupiter and Saturn orbit the Sun in nearly the same plane, called the plane of the ecliptic), which immediately reduces the number of coordinates to 12. One can also suppose that the Sun does not move, so the number of coordinates comes down to eight. Various physical processes keep some things constant (the energy, momentum, and angular momentum of the system, for example), and this reduces the number of independent coordinates. All in all, the simplest three-body problem involves only four coordinates. But even so, one of the most important problems in astronomy necessarily involved more than three variables and could be thought of as invoking a "space" of more than three dimensions. What was true of celestial mechanics also applied to theoretical mechanics, which needed the extra dimensions to be applicable to a wide variety of problems. So, spaces of more than three dimensions were not outlandish. But that didn't make them into geometrical objects, because there did not seem to be a metric involved.

Even so, the French mathematician Henri Poincaré revitalized the subject of celestial mechanics in a long memoir in 1893 by considering the orbits of celestial bodies in this four-dimensional space. He considered two massive objects moving in a fixed plane around their common center of gravity, and a 'planetoid' that also moves in that plane. This third body is so small it is affected by the gravitational pull of the two larger bodies, but does not affect them in turn. (This is adequate even for some questions about the motion of Moon in a three-body system with the Earth and the Sun.) The behavior of the planetoid is known when its two coordinates of position and its two coordinates of velocity are known, so it moves in a four-dimensional space. In this setting, Poincaré was able to prove many new results about the long-term stability of the orbit, and to show that if the planetoid does not escape, and moves only in a bounded region of this four-dimensional space, then it will return infinitely often almost exactly to any position it has occupied.

Even if mathematicians rejected the geometrical interpretation, they were stuck with problems involving many variables. The first thing to do in these cases, and it had been from the time of Descartes, is to simplify the problem by changing the variables. Why study

$$8x^2 - 3y^2 - 10xy - 4x - 8y - 3 = 0$$

when you can study

$$X^2 - Y^2 = 1?$$

(Set $x = \frac{X+Y-2}{4}$, $y = \frac{3X-Y-6}{7}$ or $X = x + 3y + 2$, $Y = 3x - y$.)

This technique was standard across mathematics long before Riemann's time. The aim was to find routine methods to reduce complicated expressions to simple ones. Every time one was found, it became part of the training of young mathematicians, and something that professional mathematicians regarded as part of their normal work.

It became inevitable for mathematicians to look for ways of simplifying expressions in any number of variables, and that came to include the expressions for Riemann's kind of metrics. This was an enterprise begun by the German mathematicians Rudolf Lipschitz and Elwin Bruno Christoffel in the 1870s and continued a generation later by the Italian mathematicians Gregorio Ricci-Curbastro and Tullio Levi-Civita. They established a variety of theorems about these formulae, initially without ever quite seeing it as geometry.

Ricci's problem was harder than the simple example given above, and not only because he had several (say n) variables to consider. The expressions he wanted to work with were of the form

$$ds^2 = g_{11}du_1^2 + 2g_{12}du_1du_2 + \cdots + g_{nn}du_n,^2$$

where the g_{jk} are functions of the variables $u_1, u_2, \ldots, u_n$. But the transformations he had to work with changed the variables; their effect on the differentials was indirect.

Ricci wrote up an extensive account of his work, covering a variety of related topics that cannot all be mentioned here, and submitted it for a Royal Prize of the Accademia dei Lincei in Rome. Beltrami reviewed this account, noting that in other works Ricci had indicated a range of uses in mathematical physics for his discoveries. Nonetheless, he wrote in his report, "a long, uninterrupted series of laboured transformations . . . make the reader's task somehow painful," calling the paper a "mighty effort of preparatory elaboration" but not "the sum of final results definitely acquired and immediately utilisable." (Bottazzini 1999, 246). Nobody won the prize that year.

Ricci tried again in 1901 when he submitted his most recent papers, as well as a manuscript on the theory of elasticity. Once again, he did not get the prize. Nevertheless, he continued to publish, but few of his peers appreciated his ideas, finding them burdensome and obscure.

It is interesting that his work proved to be exactly what Einstein needed after 1910 when he turned to study gravity. His friend and colleague Marcel Grossmann, who knew Ricci and Levi Civita's work, taught it to Einstein, and together they forged the first theory of general relativity. All of which invites the question: why were the geometric implications of Ricci's work, with its origins in Riemann's ideas, not pursued before?

The answer is fairly simple. Only with the idea that gravity was connected to the curvature of four-dimensional spacetime was there a significant reason to study what Ricci had done at such length, and only with the general theory of relativity was there a problem for which these techniques were truly indispensable.

More about the mathematics

What are polar coordinates?

They are a very convenient system of coordinates in the plane. With respect to an origin O and a fixed direction ℓ through O the polar coordinates of a point P are the distance r from O to P and the angle θ between ℓ and the line OP. The point O does not have polar coordinates.

Polar coordinates are related to (x, y) coordinates by the formulae

$$x = r \cos \theta, \quad y = r \sin \theta.$$

We could now calculate an expression for the distance between two points whose polar coordinates are given, leading to a complicated result that we shall not need. It is useful, however, to calculate the formula for two points that are very close together (see Figure 16).

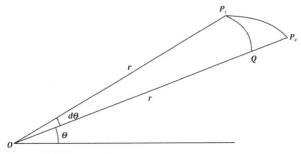

Figure 16. *Polar coordinates*

First we observe that two points Q and P_0 on the same radius and with polar coordinates (r, θ) and $(r + dr, \theta)$ respectively, are a distance dr apart. Second, points Q and P_1 on the same circle center O and a small distance apart have polar coordinates (r, θ) and $(r, \theta + d\theta)$ respectively, and the distance between them along the arc is $r d\theta$.

To find the distance from P_0 to P_1 we now use the fact that dr and $d\theta$ are very small, and deduce that the straight-line distance from Q to P_1 is very well approximated by $r d\theta$, and the angle at Q between the lines QP_0 and QP_1 is well approximated by a right-angle. This allows us to use the Pythagorean theorem to deduce that the square of the distance is very well approximated by $dr^2 + r^2 d\theta^2$.

Or, we could have argued that if $x = r \cos\theta$ then differentiation tells us that

$$dx = dr \cos\theta - r \sin\theta d\theta,$$

and similarly from $y = r \sin\theta$ we deduce that

$$dy = dr \sin\theta + r \cos\theta d\theta.$$

From this, by squaring and adding, we again deduce that

$$ds^2 = dr^2 + r^2 d\theta^2.$$

Let us move on to stereographic projection:

On the sphere of radius R centered at the origin a point P on the sphere has coordinates

$R(\sin \rho \cos \theta, \sin \rho \sin \theta, \cos \rho)$.

We map it out along the line SP to the point P' where the radius meets the horizontal plane with equation $z = R$

We are interested in the image in the horizontal plane of a very small segment on the sphere. Distances in the plane can be easily measured, and we want to know the corresponding distances on the sphere.

In the horizontal plane, we take polar coordinates as before, and we write the metric as

$$ds^2 = dr^2 + r^2 d\theta^2.$$

On the sphere, we write the metric as

$$d\sigma^2 = d\rho^2 + \sin^2 \rho d\theta^2,$$

using σ instead of S to avoid confusion.

So our task is to find a formula for $d\sigma$ that involves r, dr, θ and $d\theta$ but does not contain ρ or $d\rho$. From Figure 14, we see that angle $NSP = \tan \frac{\rho}{2}$, so the point P' has coordinates

$$(r, \theta) = (2R \tan \frac{\rho}{2}, \theta).$$

This implies that $r = 2R \tan \frac{\rho}{2}$, and so

$$dr = R \sec^2 \frac{\rho}{2} d\rho = R \left(1 + \tan^2 \frac{\rho}{2}\right) d\rho,$$

so

$$dr = R(1 + \left(\frac{r}{2R}\right)^2 d\rho$$

and

$$dr = \frac{4R^2 + r^2}{4R} d\rho.$$

So

$$dp = \frac{4R}{4R^2 + r^2} dr.$$

The trigonometric formula that connects $\sin \rho$ and $\tan \frac{\rho}{2}$ is

$$\sin \rho = 2 \frac{\tan \frac{\rho}{2}}{1 + \tan^2 \frac{\rho}{2}}$$

which implies that

$$\sin \rho = \frac{Rr}{R^2 + r^2}.$$

We use these equations to eliminate ρ and $d\rho$, and we find that

$$d\sigma^2 = \left(\frac{4R}{4R^2 + r^2}\right)^2 dr^2 + \left(\frac{4Rr}{4R^2 + r^2}\right)^2 d\theta^2.$$

This simplifies significantly, to

$$d\sigma^2 = \left(\frac{4R}{4R^2 + r^2}\right)^2 (dr^2 + r^2 d\theta^2).$$

This says that each point on the sphere, the metric on the sphere is a scale multiple of the metric on the plane. This means that a very small triangle on the sphere is mapped to a very small triangle on the plane by being scaled up. The scale factor varies, depending on where on the sphere the triangle is, and is given by the term $\frac{4R}{4R^2 + r^2}$. But because the image triangle is a scale copy of the triangle on the sphere, its angles are the same, as we claimed above; stereographic projection is conformal.

3. Complex functions

O ne of the major success stories in 19th-century mathematics was the creation of a theory of complex-valued functions of a complex variable. In 1800, even the nature of a complex number was contested; by 1900, it could be argued that more was known about complex differentiable functions than about real ones.

Complex numbers

In 1800, the relationship between the counting numbers (1, 2, 3, and so on) and the measuring numbers (arbitrary lengths including, for example, $\sqrt{2}$, π, and so on) was unclear but unproblematic in that no one worried about it. Some numbers were exact: the whole numbers or integers, and fractions. All others could be known to any level of precision in terms of their decimal expansion. Counting and measuring numbers share two kinds of properties: they can be added, subtracted, multiplied, and divided (division by zero is excluded). And they can be compared in point of size: given any two numbers, either they are equal or one is larger than the other. Counting numbers are, of course, measuring numbers, and a better name for the measuring numbers that were coming into use was the real numbers.

There were also complex numbers, solutions of an equation like $x^2 + 1 = 0$. The square of every real number is positive, so the solutions of this equation, whose squares equal -1, cannot be real. Mathematicians could deny that such numbers existed, but that left whole swathes of polynomial equations without solutions, so it was easier to allow them to exist. That raised the question of what these numbers are.

Euler came up with the first good answer: they are numbers because they can be added, subtracted, multiplied, and divided. But because they cannot be compared in point of size, they cannot measure the size of collections, so we can only have an idea of them—that is to say, they exist only in our minds and are, accordingly, imaginary numbers. The numbers i and $-i$ are of this kind, and they have the property that $i^2 = (-i)^2 = -1$.

Of course, one can mix up the real numbers and the new numbers, and get expressions of the form $a + ib$. These expressions are naturally called complex numbers, because they are a complex entity made up of two bits. But, if the usual rules of algebra apply to such numbers, then we have

$$(a + ib)(c + id) = ac + iad + ibc + i^2bd = ac + i(ad + bc) - bd = ac - bd + i(ad + bc).$$

which is a number of the same form as $a + ib$ and $c + id$. This gave rise to the hope that every solution of a polynomial equation was of this form, a claim that went by the grand name of the Fundamental Theorem of Algebra, and was first tackled by Euler, Lagrange, and Jean-Baptiste le Rond d'Alembert in the 18th century, and Gauss in the early 19th century, with steadily growing levels of rigor.

There is another way of thinking of complex numbers, which occurred to several people, notably Gauss, and later Augustin-Louis Cauchy, but several more minor figures as well. We can let the real numbers be laid out along the usual x axis, and the y axis be populated by the numbers iy, where y is a real number. Then the point (x, y) in the plane can be represented by the complex number $x + iy$. So just as every real number can be represented by a point on a line, every complex number can be represented by a point on a plane. This goes some way toward reassuring people that complex numbers do exist. It was formalized by the Irish mathematician Sir William Rowan Hamilton in 1834 and presented as a definition of what a complex number is: a pair of real numbers with the well-known rules for their arithmetic.

It was not just algebra that promoted the idea of complex numbers. Trigonometry did too. When Euler showed in 1748 that

$e^{i\theta} = \cos\theta + i\sin\theta$ he unified the theories of the exponential function and the trigonometric functions to great effect. This equation has the consequence that

$$e^{i\pi} = -1,$$

which neatly involves several of the basic constants in mathematics, although it seems that Euler himself never wrote it.

Complex numbers and variables turned up in many other problems too, most significantly in integrals. The gifted and prolific French mathematician Cauchy wrote many papers on aspects of a theory of complex functions of a complex variable, although he only began to pull his ideas together in the 1840s. Riemann read some of these papers, but when he began to publish, he immediately found the heart of the matter, as we shall shortly see.

Complex functions

Growing clarity about the nature of complex numbers, and so of a complex variable, would not of itself have pushed anyone to invent a theory of complex functions. A crucial problem that did that concerned what came to be called elliptic integrals and elliptic functions. The name was introduced because similar integrals determine arc length along an ellipse, and so they arise in specifying where the planets are in their elliptical orbits around the Sun.

Ever since the invention of the calculus, it had been known that differentiation was easy and the inverse operation, integration, was hard. Many simple-looking integrals could not be evaluated, for example

$$\int \frac{dx}{\sqrt{1 - x^4}}.$$

This was embarrassing, to say the least, and while several mathematicians, including Legendre, found things to say about this integral, its full interpretation eluded them. They had only a limited understanding of the integral as a function of its upper end point

$$f(u) = \int_0^u \frac{dx}{\sqrt{1-x^4}}.$$

Legendre had computed values of it in the range $0 \le u \le 1$, which was enough for some purposes, but otherwise, people knew very little.

Then, starting in 1826, two young mathematicians, Niels Henrik Abel in Norway and Jacobi in Prussia, solved the problem by standing it on its head. They exploited the analogy with the well-understood integral

$$v(u) = \int_0^u \frac{dx}{\sqrt{1-x^2}}$$

which can be integrated to give

$$v(u) = \arcsin(u),$$

and then turned around to say

$u = \sin v.$
Indeed, we usually evaluate the integral $v(u) = \int_0^u \frac{dx}{\sqrt{1-x^2}}$ by putting $x = \sin t$, so $dx = \cos t\, dt$, and the integral becomes

$$v = \int_0^w \cos t \frac{dt}{\sqrt{1-\sin^2 t}} = \int_0^w \frac{\cos t\, dt}{\cos t} = \int_0^w dt = w,$$

where $\sin w = u$. The many-valued "function" $v = \arcsin(u)$ is a messy object to study; on the other hand, its inverse function, $u = \sin v$ is delightful.

Abel and Jacobi independently took the integral

$$v = f(u) = \int_0^u \frac{dx}{\sqrt{1-x^4}}.$$

and treated it as defining a function $u = \rho(v)$. They both drew on problems with earlier work on this integral to conclude that the function $\rho(v)$ would be a lot easier to study if it were treated as a complex-valued function of a complex variable. There was no theory of such functions at the time, but the analogy with the trigonometric functions proved a sure guide, and their imperfect proofs of many results were mopped up later.

The resulting theory of elliptic functions generalized the theory of trigonometric functions, accomplishing everything that could be asked of it, and more. It was successful in mechanics and geometry and, as Jacobi discovered, it had deep and surprising connections to number theory. Their discovery made Abel and Jacobi famous. Unfortunately, Abel died of tuberculosis at the age of 26, before he could enjoy the recognition of his genius. Jacobi, however, went on to a successful career as a professor at Königsberg University, where he spent much of the rest of his life before dying in 1851 at the age of 46.

But in all those years, the problem of understanding more complicated integrals remained essentially unsolved. Nothing Jacobi could do, and none of the extensive insights that Abel had made, permitted more than a glimpse of what a theory of such integrals could be. This was the great task that Riemann had set for himself.

Riemann's doctoral thesis

In his doctoral thesis of 1851, Riemann argued that if a function f is a function of a single complex variable $z = x + iy$, and not two real variables x and y, then its derivative $\frac{df}{dz}$ must have an unambiguous value everywhere the function is differentiable.

By following the implications of this simple point—a hallmark of Riemann's approach to many problems was to take simple ideas seriously—he came to a profound characterization of complex differentiable functions, as the next box explains.

Complex differentiation:

By the standard rules of the calculus, the derivative of a function is the limit of the quotient

$$\frac{f(z + dz) - f(z)}{dz}$$

as dz tends to zero. Riemann insisted that it must take the same value however dz tends to zero. For example, we could let it take only real values, or let it take only purely imaginary ones.

In the first case $dz = dx$ and the quotient becomes

$$\frac{f(z + dx) - f(z)}{dx} = \frac{f(x + iy + dx) - f(x + iy)}{dx},$$

and in the limit this is the partial derivative of f with respect to x.

Similarly, in the second case $dz = idy$ and the quotient becomes

$$\frac{f(z + idy) - f(z)}{idy} = -i\left(\frac{f(z + idy) - f(z)}{dy}\right) =$$

$$-i\left(\frac{f(x + i(y + dy)) - f(x + iy)}{dy}\right)$$

and in the limit this is $-i$ times the partial derivative of f with respect to y.

If we write $f = u + iv$, where u and v are real-valued functions of $x + iy$, and the partial derivatives with respect to x and y as $f_x = u_x + iu_y$ and $f_y = u_y + iv_y$ respectively, then the first calculation produced

$f_x = u_x + iv_x$ and the second one produced $-if_y = -i(u_y + iv_y) = -iu_y + v_y$. If these are equal, then

$$u_x = v_y \quad \text{and} \quad u_y = -v_x.$$

The argument can be reversed (to be precise, under some small technical conditions we can ignore here) and any function $u + iv = f(x + iy)$ that obeys the above equations is complex differentiable as a function of $z = x + iy$.

When a function f of a complex variable $x + iy$ takes complex values, these values can be written as a sum of their real and imaginary parts, so we may write

$$f(x + iy) = u(x + iy) + iv(x + iy),$$

where both u and v are real-valued functions. If we now write the partial derivatives of u with respect to x and y as u_x and u_y respectively, and likewise write the partial derivatives of v with respect to x and y as v_x and v_y, then the above box shows that for a complex differentiable function we have the equations

$$u_x = v_y \quad \text{and} \quad u_y = -v_x.$$

Because of their importance, the equations have been taken as the characteristic sign of a complex function, and in honor of their discoverers they are known as the Cauchy-Riemann equations.

The Cauchy-Riemann equations have two remarkable implications. Riemann immediately deduced, as Cauchy had not, that a complex map is conformal, unless its derivative vanishes. This was a conclusion known to Gauss, and Riemann could well have learned it from his 1826 paper on conformal maps—or even, perhaps, by talking to Gauss. The second is found by differentiating u and v once more and using the Cauchy-Riemann equations. The result is that the real and imaginary parts of a complex function satisfy the equations

$$\frac{\partial^2 u}{\partial x^2} + \frac{\partial^2 u}{\partial y^2} = 0, \quad \frac{\partial^2 v}{\partial x^2} + \frac{\partial^2 v}{\partial y^2} = 0.$$

This means that u and v are what are called harmonic functions, and a great deal was known about harmonic functions by then, because they had turned up in the theories of gravitation, electricity, and magnetism. For instance, it was known that the value of a harmonic function at a point is the average of its values on any circle centered at that point. This implies that a harmonic function can take its maximal and minimal values only on the boundary of its domain of definition because a function whose maximal value is its average value must be constant.

In the 1830s and 1840s, after the work of Gauss (and also of the English mathematician George Green, although it was less well-known), it was widely believed that a harmonic function can be defined on any region bounded by a single closed curve that does not cross itself, and is uniquely determined by the values that it takes on the boundary. I shall call such a region disc-shaped, but it can obviously have any of a huge variety of shapes. Dirichlet had lectured on this problem, claiming that the belief was valid. He said that this was so by a principle that said the integral

$$\int (u_x^2 + v_x^2) dx dy$$

taken over the region, where u is any function that takes the given values on the boundary, takes its lower bound. It is then straightforward to show that this minimizing function u is harmonic.

The task of establishing Dirichlet's claim became known as the Dirichlet problem, and Dirichlet's principle would solve Dirichlet's problem—if it were true. Unfortunately, Dirichlet's argument in defense of the principle was that the integral is an integral of positive terms, it is always greater than zero, and so it has a greatest lower bound. It is true that the values have a greatest lower bound, but it is not clear that there is a function u for which the integral attains the lower bound. After all, the function $f(x) = 1/x$ is defined for all positive x and is always positive, but there is no x for which it takes the value zero.

Another problem is that a function u may always take small values, say between 1 and 2, and yet its derivatives u_x and u_y take very large values. The derivatives are measuring the slope of the function at each point, so if the function given on the boundary oscillates rapidly, the derivatives will be large even though the function is small. After Riemann's death, his former student, Friedrich Prym, showed that these oscillations could even make the Dirichlet integral infinite. In that case, every candidate function u returns an infinite value for the Dirichlet integral, and there is no question of it having a lower bound, attained or not.

Every physicist of the time believed in the Dirichlet principle, as well as in the existence of a solution to the Dirichlet problem. In the case, for example, of electric charge, the principle says that given a conductor and a distribution of charge on its surface, there is a harmonic potential function determining the force on a unit electric charge at any point outside the conductor. This was their experience; even after Riemann's time, leading physicists such as James Clerk Maxwell and Hermann von Helmholtz continued to believe the theorem and could not understand why mathematicians thought there was anything to prove.

Mathematicians, however, need proofs of theorems. Among them, Riemann was not entirely happy with Dirichlet's principle and sketched a proof of it that was unconvincing. On that basis, he argued that to define a complex function on a domain, it is enough to determine its real and imaginary parts. In fact, by the Cauchy-Riemann equations, it may be enough to define one of them, say the real part, by prescribing a harmonic function on the domain, because the imaginary part is then determined up to the choice of an arbitrary constant (as we discuss below). If the imaginary part is single-valued (like z^n, where n is an integer, but not like $\log z$), then it and the given real part define a complex function. If the domain is bounded by a single curve that does not cross itself, then it is enough to define a function on the boundary of the domain, because the solution of Dirichlet's problem provides the harmonic function on the interior of the domain.

In this way, Riemann laid down all the basics of complex function with no more work than had already been expended on the theory of harmonic functions—what could be better than that? It is even a two-way street: at least on disc-shaped domains, every harmonic function must be the real or imaginary part of a complex function. It is easier to find complex functions than harmonic ones, so complex function theory can help make harmonic function theory easier. As the distinguished 20th-century mathematician Lars Ahlfors noted in 1953, Riemann "virtually puts equality signs between two-dimensional potential theory and complex function theory."

Complex functions, however, raise problems of their own. If you write down the simplest complex functions, say $f(z) = z$, or let f be given by a polynomial in z, it is clear that you can give it a value "at infinity," indeed, the value infinity. Or you can say that as the absolute value of z gets bigger and bigger, so does the absolute value of $f(z)$, and it does so without limit. This is not true for a function like $f(z) = 1/z$, but this function is infinite when $z = 0$.

What you cannot do is find a non-trivial complex function f that such that $|f(z)|$ is bounded for all values of $|z|$. This is based on the fact that the real and imaginary parts would likewise be bounded everywhere and would, therefore, take a maximum value somewhere, but harmonic functions cannot take their maximum values other than at boundary points, and in this case, the domain has no boundary. So, as you can see from our earlier remarks, a complex function that meets all these requirements is a constant.

Riemann needed a solution to Dirichlet's problem that allowed for functions to be harmonic everywhere except at a finite number of points, where they became infinite in the way that $\log(z)$ does at the origin. To his credit, he attempted to do exactly that. Later generations of mathematicians, writing at a time when counterexamples to Dirichlet's principle were known, criticized him for relying on the principle, but he did not. He did attempt to say that the space of candidate functions u was not like the positive real line but was closed, and so the lower bound would be attained. That said, he was not able to create the theory that would eventually allow claims of this sort to be made precise and, sometimes, proved.

Even so, Riemann had given an insightful and precise definition of what a complex-valued function of a complex variable is, showing that its real and imaginary parts are each harmonic functions. He had good reasons to believe that a harmonic function is known completely on a region of a disc-shaped region if it is known on the boundary of that region, if its values agree with some continuous real-valued function on the boundary. This allowed him to believe, almost correctly as later mathematicians proved, that every complex function arises in this way.

Riemann was now in a position to claim that there are complex functions defined on every disc-shaped domain. Intuitively and informally, all such domains are topologically the same: there is a continuous map from one to the other and back. Does that mean that all these domains admit essentially the same complex functions? Or are there different types of functions on different domains? Riemann's answer was that, for the purpose of complex function theory, all these domains are equivalent. This result is known today as the Riemann mapping theorem. Its proof, however, required much more attention to detail, and much more insight into what could go wrong, than Riemann was able to provide.

Abelian functions

Riemann's innovations did not stop with his thesis of 1851. In fact, they had barely begun. Up until then, most mathematicians expected a real-valued function of a real variable to be defined for every real number, unless it could not be. For example, the function

$$f(x) = \frac{1}{x - 1} + 23 + 4x - 117x^3$$

makes sense for every value of x except $x = 1$ (because one cannot divide by zero). The only way mathematicians' expectations could be dashed was if the function was defined by an infinite power series, such as

$$f(x) = 1 + 2x + 4x^2 + 8x^3 + \cdots,$$

which converges for $|x| < 1/2$, but otherwise is not defined (if you try adding up the terms of this infinite series when $|x| > 1/2$, its value can be made as large as you like). Naturally, they extended the same expectations to complex-valued functions of a complex variable.

In Riemann's view, however, this tied the concept of a complex function to the way it could be represented. Instead, he noted that all that was necessary for a function of $z = x + iy$ to be a complex function was for its real and imaginary parts to satisfy the Cauchy-Riemann equations. Thus, it is possible for a complex function to be defined on any two-dimensional domain or surface, and that is what Riemann developed.

There are three seemingly distinct ways for a mathematician to come across surfaces, which can be called the algebraic, the geometric, and the pictorial.

Algebraically, a surface arises every time a mathematician writes down a polynomial equation in two complex variables, z and w. Consider, for example, the equation $y^2 = 1 - x^4$. If we work with real variables, this is a curve defined in the range $-1 \leq x \leq 1$ and for each such value of x other than 1 and -1, there are two values of y; $x = \pm 1$ implies $y = 0$.

But if we let x and y be complex, and write them as z and w, respectively, so that the equation becomes

$$w^2 = 1 - z^4,$$

then a much more complicated and informative picture emerges.

Now z has two coordinates, its real and imaginary parts, and so too does w; therefore, the equation defines a subset of four-dimensional space. There is one equation connecting the real parts, and another connecting the imaginary parts, so we are dealing with a two-dimensional domain of points—a surface—in four-dimensional space.

Four-dimensional vision is not something we come equipped with, but Riemann described an easier way to proceed: the equation tells us that for each value of z other than $1, -1, i$, and $-i$, there are two values of w. The exceptional points are where $w = 0$, as we see by writing the equation as

$$w^2 = (1 - z)(1 + z)(1 + iz)(1 - iz).$$

For every other value of z, and there are two (equal and opposite) values of w that satisfy the equation. We arrange for one set of the possible choices of w to be distributed in one copy of the plane of complex numbers that is spread out over the complex z-plane, and the other set to be similarly distributed in a second plane. These two planes share the four points where $w = 0$, and are somehow joined up in a space of four dimensions.

How they are joined up remains a mystery, but Riemann was not one to be bothered by making the surface easy to see. Quite rightly, he posited that the equation $w^2 = 1 - z^4$ clearly defines a two-dimensional surface in four-dimensional space, its points have coordinates of the form (z, w) where $w^2 = 1 - z^4$, and as a result there are two corresponding w values for each value of z other than $1, -1, i$, and $-i$. If it is not clear what this looks like, then there is no need to worry about it until you have to. Mathematicians who came after Riemann could not proceed without dealing with that concern, and they found ways to make the surface visible; Riemann, however, was content to do just the minimum necessary.

Indeed, he took the view that if you have a polynomial equation of degree k in z and m in w, then for each value of z there will generally be m values of w, although sometimes there will be fewer. The corresponding surface—today called the Riemann surface associated to the equation—can still be thought of as spread out in m sheets over the z-domain, which is most convenient to think of as a sphere rather than as a plane (use stereographic projection).

Geometrically, one starts with a surface spread out over the z plane with the property that for each value of z there will generally be m values of w, although at a finite number of points there will be fewer. Remarkably, Riemann showed that every surface defined in this way can be associated to a polynomial equation of degree k in z and m in w, so the geometric and algebraic points of view coincide.

Pictorially, Riemann asked: what two-dimensional domains are there? The crucial feature they must possess is that they must be a collection of points, every point of which can be surrounded by a disc, all of whose points also lie in the collection (think of a bunch of overlapping discs). The sphere is one, the plane another. Any region of the plane will be one if it meets the criterion above.

So are shapes you can imagine being made of paper but which do not necessarily lie in the plane. But now a second criterion has to be stated: at any point in any region of the complex plane there will be a segment parallel to the x axis and another parallel to the y axis, and the x axis part is mapped onto the y axis part by a quarter-turn anti-clockwise. This gives the region a sense of orientation, and any complex map preserves this orientation: a region is mapped by a complex map onto a region with the same orientation. This means that paper shapes can only be candidates for domains of a complex function if they can be oriented. The cylinder is allowed, but the Möbius band—a surface with only one side and one boundary—is not. Shapes made out of tubes are also allowed, provided they meet the two criteria just stated. In this way, we get the torus, the two-holed torus, and more generally the n-holed torus. (A torus is a surface of revolution generated by revolving a circle in three-dimensional space about an axis coplanar with the circle).

Figure 17. A torus

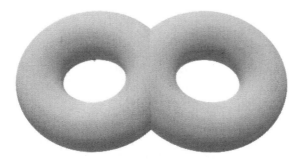

Figure 18. A two-holed torus

Riemann also allowed one or more disc-like regions to be removed from these surfaces, to give surfaces with boundaries. Points on the boundary have neighborhoods that look more-or-less like filled-in semicircles or half-discs.

This gave Riemann a vast collection of surfaces, and only a few of them had ever been taken seriously by mathematicians before. So although all of them might matter, Riemann's first task was to arrange this horde of new surfaces into manageable families, and then to find a use for at least some of them.

There was a limited precedent for that kind of information. The mathematicians Johann Listing and August Ferdinand Möbius, who were associates of Gauss, had been thinking about what surfaces there might be. They allowed two surfaces to count as the same if one could be deformed into the other without altering the relative positions of the points. Stretching, cutting and regluing are allowed if the cuts are glued back so that everything along them is as it was before. They called this type of mathematics analysis situs (Latin for analysis of position), which was a reference back to some vague ideas of Leibniz, or topology (from the Greek: topos or place, logos for word or study).

With striking prescience, Riemann began by making what has proved to be a truly fundamental distinction between surfaces that are topologically distinct. For example, surfaces with no boundary, such as the sphere, are different from surfaces with boundaries, such as the unit disc.

Among surfaces without boundaries, there is the sphere, and the ones made of tubes, including the torus. Riemann claimed (an argument later refined by others), that if you took a surface without boundary, marked a point P on it, and drew a closed non-intersecting curve on the surface that returned to the point P then one of two things could happen. The curve might divide the surface into two bits, or it might not. If every such curve did divide the surface into two pieces, the surface was a sphere.

In the second case, one could now consider drawing a second curve that started and finished somewhere on the first curve, and so on. If the surface was a torus, one could draw two curves in this way without dividing the surface into regions, but not three curves.

Riemann claimed that every surface without boundary admitted a certain maximum number of curves that do not divide it (and this number was always even). In other words, for every surface, there is number $2p$ of curves that do not divide the surface, but any system of $2p + 1$ curves constructed according to his rules must divide the surface. So, the number p, later called the genus of the surface because it captures a very general feature of surfaces, characterizes surfaces without boundaries. This number p is 0 for the sphere, 1 for the torus, and the n-holed torus has genus n.

Then he proposed a finer classification. If two surfaces were topologically the same, did that mean that they had essentially the same complex functions defined on them? As we saw above, the Riemann mapping theorem says that the unit disc and a surface S with a single boundary (and which is therefore topologically a disc) are such that every complex function defined on S is equivalent to one defined on the unit disc.

Riemann saw that the same argument would not always work for any two topologically equivalent surfaces. For example, consider the ring-shaped region lying between the circles of radii 1 and 2, and the ring-shaped region lying between the circles of radii 2 and 3. They are topologically the same, but it turns out that there is no complex map from one to the other because they have different ratios of inner to outer radius ($\frac{1}{2} \neq \frac{2}{3}$). As a result, complex functions on the one annulus are not equivalent to ones on the other, a fact which had already been noticed in the theory of elliptic functions.

If we glue the inner and outer circles of an annulus together, we get a torus, so the same argument shows that there are tori that are not equivalent for the purposes of complex function theory, specifically for the purposes of elliptic function theory.

As you can see, Riemann's opinion of the possible domain of a complex function was much clearer and more general than those of his contemporaries, which is often an indication of a really good idea. In his view, a surface is made up in an orientable way of two-dimensional neighborhoods of its points. But once again, we can ask why is it important? Are there occasions when the new generality helps with existing problems? The answer, as Riemann proceeded to show, was a resounding yes.

As we saw above, in the late 1820s Abel and Jacobi had taken the integral

$$v = f(u) = \int_0^u \frac{dx}{\sqrt{1 - x^4}}.$$

and treated it as defining a function $u = \rho(v)$ where, moreover, they let the variables u and v be complex (entirely formally, they had no theory of complex functions). They had, in fact, showed how to do this for any integral of the form

$$v = \int_0^u \frac{dx}{\sqrt{q(x)}}.$$

where $q(x)$ is a polynomial of degree 3 or 4 in x.

They also exploited the analogy with the sine and cosine functions to deduce the important property of any elliptic function, ρ, that it has two periods, complex numbers ω_1 and ω_2, such that

$$\rho(z) = \rho(z + \omega_1) = \rho(z + \omega_2).$$

By comparison, the sine and cosine functions are periodic with period 2π:

$$\sin(t) = \sin(t + 2\pi), \quad \cos(t) = \cos(t + 2\pi).$$

(There is some small print, the quotient ω_1/ω_2 cannot be real.)

By the 1850s, elliptic function theory had become one of the great examples of what a theory of complex functions might contain. There was, however, a problem: because the square root in the integrand had two distinct values it seemed impossible, as Jacobi lamented, to use Cauchy's ideas about complex functions to re-derive the theory. This left many issues obscure, and a search was on for a new way of deriving the theory. Gauss, who had come to many of these ideas 20 years before Abel and Jacobi but published almost none of them, had already looked for an answer in terms of power series methods, and without knowing this Jacobi did the same. A generation later, Weierstrass concluded the process, finally making the entire theory a part of complex function theory.

But in between Jacobi's work in the 1830s and Weierstrass's in the 1870s, Riemann solved the problem geometrically, by interpreting the integrand and its square root. He could do this because, in his view, the equation between complex variables defined a surface. By exploiting geometry and his new topology, he showed that integrals of the form $\int \frac{dx}{\sqrt{1-x^2}}$ are connected to the sphere, and all elliptic integrals are connected to the torus. The two periods of an elliptic function are directly connected to the two fundamental types of closed paths that one can draw on a torus.

Success with elliptic functions inspired mathematicians to confront many other integrals they could not evaluate, for example

$$\int \frac{dx}{\sqrt{p(x)}},$$

where $p(x)$ is a polynomial in x of degree 5 or more. This can be written as

$$\int \frac{dx}{\sqrt{y}}, \quad y^2 = p(x),$$

which was known as a hyper-elliptic integral. It in turn invited Abel, followed by Jacobi and other mathematicians, to consider the even harder integral,

$$\int f(x,y)dx, \quad \text{where } g(x,y) = 0,$$

where $f(x,y)$ is an arbitrary rational function (a quotient of two polynomials) in the complex variables x and y and $g(x,y)$ is a given, fixed, polynomial in x and y. After Abel's death, these were known as Abelian integrals.

The first breakthrough in the study of these integrals came in 1854 and 1856, when Weierstrass, who was at the time a little-known high school teacher in his early 40s in East Prussia, showed what could be done in the hyper-elliptic case. He was promptly brought to Berlin, soon becoming one of the three leaders of the most powerful Mathematics Department in the world. Remarkable though this was, Riemann's success with the general case in 1857 was even more impressive—so much so, that on reading it Weierstrass withdrew his own paper on the subject from publication and did not write on it again until 1869.

Riemann showed that all the more complicated integrals of the form

$$\int f(x, y)dx, \quad \text{where } g(x, y) = 0,$$

are connected to n-holed toruses for some appropriate value of n. More precisely, they are connected to p-holed toruses where p is the genus of the surface defined by the equation $g(x, y) = 0$.

The genus p, he showed, is equal to the number of independent integrals with no infinities on the surface; every other integral of this kind on the surface is a linear combination of these basic ones. The bafflingly complicated behavior of integrals in this setting was considerably simplified, and earlier insights of Jacobi, Abel, and Weierstrass could be fitted into a clearer picture.

One of the most famous results in all advanced mathematics came out of this research: the Riemann-Roch theorem. Riemann came up with an inequality involving the number of different functions there could be on a surface that have no more than a given number of infinities, and his student Gustav Roch introduced an extra term that made the inequality into an equality. The Riemann-Roch theorem says that every function on the Riemann sphere must have at least one infinity—all such functions are of the form

$$f(z) = \frac{az + b}{cz + d},$$

where a, b, c, d are constants and $ad - bc \neq 0$. It says that all such functions on the torus (the elliptic functions) must have at least two infinities (which was also already known). It deals similarly with all the surfaces of higher genus, and with all the questions where the functions are allowed to have more than the minimum number of infinities. In a certain sense, function theory on any complex domain was now laid bare. Analogous theorems in many domains of mathematics are to this day called Riemann-Roch theorems.

It might seem that a new period of research could begin once other mathematicians caught up with Riemann. In 1863, by which time Riemann was seriously ill, the young Rudolf Clebsch was the first to take up the challenge of understanding and then using what Riemann had outlined. When Clebsch died unexpectedly of diphtheria in 1872, seven mathematicians wrote his obituary, describing some of the difficulties that Riemann had left for his followers to sort out. One of these was the difficulty in seeing the true shape of a Riemann surface, an oddly consoling fact down the decades.

Immediate consequences

Relations between Riemann and Weierstrass were cordial. They met in Berlin, and Weierstrass proposed Riemann to the Berlin Academy of Sciences. But although Weierstrass was impressed by the younger man's insights, he had no desire to work in his geometrical and topological manner, which he believed to be imprecise. And soon after his own arrival in Berlin, he acquired a follower who was to pursue Weierstrass's preferred method aggressively, and that was Hermann Amandus Schwarz.

Weierstrass's tools were algebra and the theory of convergent power series. His lifelong goal was to accomplish for Abelian integrals what Abel and Jacobi had brought about for elliptic integrals, and to do this he worked with a theory of convergent power series in several variables. In the end, however, he published more claims—or conjectures, if you wish—than proved results. That said, he also discovered many of the most important theorems in the theory of complex functions of a single variable, and much of his reputation today rests on these by-products of his attempt to give a rigorous account of that subject.

These rigorous methods, and the disconcerting ease with which Riemann had thrown ideas into the subject, were the principal target of Schwarz's work. He was known for his eagerness for a fight, being once compared to a Cossack cavalryman; French mathematicians thought of him as vain and keen to win supporters among the younger generation of mathematicians. He set himself the task of either finding fault with Riemann's work, or of finding better, more Weierstrassian, proofs of correct results.

This was often necessary. Schwarz's solution to the Dirichlet problem provides a good example. He showed that if the problem could be solved for two domains independently, then it could be solved for any domain formed by the overlap of these two domains (provided their boundaries cross nicely). Since it could be solved for a disc-shaped domain, and for any shape that is the image of a disc by a complex function, Schwarz's method solves the Dirichlet problem for a huge collection of cases. For many years, this was the best argument known, and it was to inspire the next generation of proofs.

Deeper faults in Riemann's approach were to be found by Weierstrass, but later mathematicians found ways to recover Riemann's ideas in a rigorous way and unite them with Weierstrass's insights. Today Cauchy, Riemann, and Weierstrass are known as the three founding fathers of complex analysis.

More about the mathematics

Another important point to remember is that complex maps are conformal maps.

A map of the plane to itself is conformal if it maps the metric to a multiple of itself at every point because, as we saw when discussing stereographic projection, it then appears as a scaling at each point, and scaling preserves angles.

So the map $(x, y) \to (u(x, y), v(x, y))$ is conformal if and only if $E(x, y) = G(x, y)$ and $F(x, y) = 0$, where

$$E(x, y) = u_x(x, y)^2 + v_y(x, y)^2,$$
$$F(x, y) = u_x(x, y)u_y(x, y) + v_x(x, y)v_y(x, y),$$

and

$$G(x, y) = u_y(x, y)^2 + v_y(x, y)^2.$$

But these conclusions are immediate from the Cauchy-Riemann equations, unless the derivative of the map, and therefore its various partial derivatives, vanish. We deduce that a complex map is angle-preserving everywhere that its derivative does not vanish.

4. Primes and the zeta function

R iemann often found it profitable to take a problem involving real-valued functions of a real variable and investigate whether it could be expressed in terms of complex-valued functions of a complex variable (an attitude he might well have learned from Gauss, who had espoused it in letters to friends). Nowhere did this meet with more success than in his study of the distribution of the prime numbers. His surprising discoveries built on the work of Gauss and especially of Euler, and is embodied in his creation of the mysterious Riemann zeta function that hides its deepest secrets to this day.

The distribution of the primes

The prime numbers—the integers greater than 1 that are divisible only by themselves and 1—exert a powerful hold on mathematicians. They are, of course, the building blocks of all the integers: every number is the product of prime numbers in an essentially unique way. For example,

$$60 = 2^2 \times 3 \times 5,$$

and apart from the order of the factors, there is no other way of writing 60 as a product of prime numbers.

But this is not the main reason for the respect that mathematicians pay to prime numbers, and the intensity with which they study them—an intensity that Riemann did much to heighten.

That was articulated well by the distinguished number-theorist

Don Zagier. In his 1975 inaugural lecture at the University of Bonn he noted:

> There are two facts of which I hope to convince you so overwhelmingly that they will permanently be engraved in your hearts. The first is that the prime numbers belong to the most arbitrary objects studied by mathematicians: they grow like weeds, seeming to obey no other law than that of chance, and nobody can predict where the next one will sprout. The second fact is even more astonishing, for it states just the opposite: that the prime numbers exhibit stunning regularity, that there are laws governing their behaviour, and that they obey these laws with almost military precision.

Sometimes primes occur close together: 2, 3, 5, 7, 11. But even if we look at larger primes, which you might expect to be further apart, we still find primes that differ by only 2. For example, 2267 and 2269, and 7331 and 7333. In fact, the list of these twin primes (on the web) seems to go on forever and is a conjecture that indeed there are infinitely many twin primes.

But there are also large gaps between consecutive primes: after 887, the next prime is 907, a gap of 20. Indeed, one can engineer arbitrarily large gaps. To have a gap of 137, say, consider the sequence

$$138! + 2, 138! + 3, \ldots, 138! + 138$$

$138!$ is the number

$$138 \times 137 \times 136 \ldots \times 2$$

so $138! + 2$ is divisible by 2, $138! + 3$ is divisible by 3, and so on, all the way to $138! + 138$, which is divisible by 138. This gives us a run of 137 consecutive numbers and, as promised, none of them are prime.

However, you might reasonably feel that this example is contrived: $138!$ is a huge number of 237 digits. You might well feel that a gap of 137 (a three-digit number) is very small when compared to such a monster.

Are the gaps between each prime and the next generally small, relative to the size of the prime? One way to answer this question would be to have a formula that generates successive primes—but no such formula has ever been found. Or, we might like to have a formula that tells us, given a prime number, what the next one is; again, there is no such formula. It is for simple reasons like these that mathematicians regard the behavior of the primes as highly arbitrary.

Faced with an unpredictable phenomenon of any kind, a good instinct is to collect data. Perhaps what appears to be turbulent close up, may look smooth and orderly from further away.

So, starting in Gauss's day, mathematicians began to make lists of primes and survey when they occur. A natural number to count is the number of primes less than or equal to a number x. This number is denoted $\pi(x)$.

A table of the number of primes

x	$\pi(x)$	$x/\pi(x)$
10	4	2.5
100	25	4.0
1 000	168	6.0
10 000	1229	8.1
100 000	9 592	10.4
1 000 000	78 498	12.7
10 000 000	664 579	15.0
100 000 000	5 761 455	17.4
1 000 000 000	50 847 534	19.7

We can check this. For example, when $x = 10^9 = 1000000000$ the value of $\ln(x)$ is $20.72326584\ldots$ and $10^9/20.72326584 = 48254042.43$. This is not far off the exact value of the number of primes less than 1,000,000,000, which is $50,847,534$. For the first time, there is something predictable and regular to say about the primes.What is striking about this table is that, after a slightly rocky start, the value of $\pi(x)$ seems to increase by about 2.3 from one line to the next. This suggested to Gauss when he was only 15 that perhaps the increase was approximately the natural logarithm of 10, $\ln 10 = \log_e(10) = 2.302585093\ldots$. That would mean that $x/\pi(x)$ was increasing at the same rate as $\ln(x)$ and so that $\pi(x)$ was increasing at the same rate as $x/\ln(x)$. More precisely, this would mean that the ratio of $\pi(x)$ to $x/\ln(x)$ tends to 1 as x goes up indefinitely, so that for large values of x the value of $\pi(x)$—the number of primes less than or equal to x—is close to the value of $x/\ln(x)$.

Computations like these speak forcefully to mathematicians, and the idea that the number of primes less than or equal to x is increasingly close to the value of $x/\ln(x)$ was investigated from several points of view in the 19th century until it was eventually proved independently by the French mathematician Jacques Hadamard and the Belgian mathematician Charles de la Vallée Poussin in 1896.

Riemann's contribution to the story lies deeper than theirs and is still not fully worked out. It is difficult to describe, but we can get some impression of it. Riemann addressed the next natural questions that arise while comparing $\pi(x)$ and $x/\ln(x)$: how good is this approximation? Can we find a better one?

Gauss himself had suggested this improvement:

$$Li(x) = \int_0^x \frac{dt}{\ln(t)},$$

a function called the logarithmic integral. Like $\pi(x)$, this is a slowly growing function, and for example

$$Li(10^9) = 50849234.96,$$

which is a very good approximation to the number of primes less than 1,000,000,000, and better than the previous one.

What are we to make of the logarithmic integral as an approximation to $\pi(x)$, supposing that it could be proved to be as good as it looks? The flaw here is that it grows steadily, whereas $\pi(x)$ grows in fits and starts. This is where the unpredictability of the primes comes back into the story. There are runs of integers that contain more than the expected number of primes, and regions that contain fewer. A really good approximation to $\pi(x)$ would similarly speed up and slow down, suggesting that a better approximation would be a sum of terms, some positive and some negative, and that is what Riemann was able to produce.

To obtain his formula, Riemann went back to a much earlier study of the prime numbers. Back in the 1740s, Euler had discovered a splendid formula about the integers:

$$\prod \left(1 - \frac{1}{p^k}\right)^{-1} = 1 + \frac{1}{2^k} + \frac{1}{3^k} + \cdots .$$

It is easiest to check when $k = 1$. In this case, the left-hand side is

$$\left(1 - \frac{1}{2}\right)^{-1} \left(1 - \frac{1}{3}\right)^{-1} \left(1 - \frac{1}{5}\right)^{-1} \cdots .$$

Each term in this infinite product can be expanded as an infinite series (in fact, as a geometric progression). For example:

$$\left(1 - \frac{1}{2}\right)^{-1} = 1 + \frac{1}{2} + \frac{1}{2^2} + \frac{1}{2^3} + \cdots ,$$

$$\left(1 - \frac{1}{3}\right)^{-1} = 1 + \frac{1}{3} + \frac{1}{3^2} + \frac{1}{3^3} + \cdots ,$$

and so on.

On the right hand-side, we have

$$1 + \frac{1}{2} + \frac{1}{3} + \frac{1}{4} + \frac{1}{5} + \cdots .$$

So let's do a spot check: can the term $1/2^2.3.5$ occur on each side?

On the right-hand side, the answer is obvious: $2^2.3.5 = 60$, so it is the 60th term on the right-hand side. On the left-hand side, we can get it by taking the term in $1/2^2$ from the first infinite series, the term in $1/3$ from the second infinite series, and the term in $1/5$ from the third infinite series. Moreover, because each number is a product of primes in an essentially unique way, we can only get the term $1/2^2.3.5$ in this way.

What works for the term we chose works for any term, and it continues to work if we replace p by p^k, so we can conclude that Euler's product formula holds:

$$\prod\left(1 - \frac{1}{p^k}\right)^{-1} = 1 + \frac{1}{2^k} + \frac{1}{3^k} + \cdots.$$

But we should be a little more careful. We are dealing with infinite series and infinite products, and we have to make sure that they make numerical sense. In the present case, it is well known that

$$1 + \frac{1}{2} + \frac{1}{3} + \frac{1}{4} + \cdots$$

can be made arbitrarily large by adding together enough terms, so we should not speak of the product formula when $k = 1$.

On the other hand, it can be shown that

$$1 + \frac{1}{2^k} + \frac{1}{3^k} + \cdots$$

converges to a finite number for any real number k greater than 1 (k need not now be an integer). Mathematicians speak of this sum as a function of k that they call the zeta function — the name zeta goes back to Euler — and which they write as $\zeta(k)$. The Euler product formula means that this function can be written in two ways, as a sum, and as a product, and that gives mathematicians two chances of proving something about it.

Riemann's first contribution was to replace the real variable k by a complex variable, which he wrote s. He showed that the infinite sum

$$1 + \frac{1}{2^s} + \frac{1}{3^s} + \cdots$$

converges, provided the real part of s is greater than 1. This is reasonable, because

$$e^{x+iy} = e^x e^{iy} = e^x(\cos y + i \sin y),$$

so it is the real part, x, of $x + iy$ that determines the size of e^{x+iy}.

Why do this? Riemann was too much of a mathematician to say, but what he knew very well and proceeded to exploit was Cauchy's discovery that integrals in the complex plane can often be evaluated as sums. This goes back to the first quirk anyone encounters when learning the calculus. Differentiation works smoothly for every integer

$$\frac{d}{dx}x^n = nx^{n-1},$$

but integration has an extra detail:

$$\int x^n dx = \frac{x^{n+1}}{n+1}, \ n \neq -1, \text{ and } \int x^{-1} dx = \ln x.$$

In the complex plane, let us integrate z^{-1} around the circle C center the origin and radius 1 defined by $z = e^{it}$. We have $dz = ie^{it}dt$, and so $z^{-1}dz = idt$, and so we obtain

$$\int_C z^{-1}dz = \int_0^{2\pi} idt = 2\pi i,$$

and the resulting value of the integral is $2\pi i$.

Suitably generalized, this means that the integral of any complex function around a closed curve turns up as a sum that has to do with points $z = a$ where the function is well approximated by the function $\alpha/(z-a)$. More precisely, the contribution of that point is $2\pi i\alpha$.

This gave Riemann a chance to evaluate the sum

$$1 + \frac{1}{2^s} + \frac{1}{3^s} + \cdots$$

by finding a way to evaluate certain integrals around appropriate contours.

But there might seem to be a problem: the sum is only defined when the real part of s is greater than 1. However, there is an easy way out. Consider the function $1/(1-x)$. It is defined for every $x \neq 1$, but the corresponding power series

$$\frac{1}{1-x} = 1 + x + x^2 + x^3 + \cdots$$

is only defined for $-1 < x < 1$. If this argument is run in reverse, it shows that we can hope to start with a power series with a limited range of definition and pass to a function with a much greater range of definition.

That is the case with the zeta function. In this way, Riemann obtained a function that is defined for all complex values of s other than $s = 1$ and which agrees with the infinite series

$$1 + \frac{1}{2^s} + \frac{1}{3^s} + \cdots$$

whenever that series converges. This function has been called the Riemann zeta function ever since Riemann introduced it.

The points where the zeta function is zero are particularly important. They are of two kinds. The so-called trivial zeros occur at the negative even integers. The interesting zeros are much more elusive.

Riemann noticed a curious fact about the zeta function: the values of $\zeta(s)$ and $\zeta(1 - s)$ are nearly the same. As put, that is wrong, but he found a way of multiplying the zeta function by another function to obtain a function $\xi(s)$ with the property that

$$\xi(s) = \xi(1 - s).$$

This means that the function $\xi(s)$ is symmetric about the line in the complex plane where the real part of s is $1/2$, and this property passes in an attenuated form to the zeta function. Because the function was obtained by multiplying the function by something non-zero, the zeros of the function must be symmetrically situated around the same line.

Now, zeros of a complex function are points where the logarithm of the function is infinite, so they too can be picked up by complex integration, and sums of them can be evaluated. Riemann discovered that the more precisely the zeros of zeta could be located, the more appropriately a contour around them could be drawn, and so the distribution of the primes could be determined more accurately. He showed that the first few zeros all lie on the line (he did not publish this part of his investigations and it was only found well after his death), and he even conjectured that all the non-trivial zeros lie on the line. His comment was:

> A rigorous proof of this would certainly be desirable; however, after a few brief and fruitless attempts to find one, I have put this on one side for the time being, because it did not seem to be essential to the immediate object of my investigation.

Attempts have been made ever since, and the best have yielded some answers, although the conjecture remains unsolved to this day.

Riemann's conjecture matters for many reasons. The simplest is that it is equivalent to the statement that the deviation of the number of primes from the estimate $Li(x)$ is some constant multiple of $\sqrt{x}log(x)$ as x increases.

The alternative that the Riemann hypothesis is false has dramatic implications. In his essay for the Millennium Prizes Book, which features 23 problems that set much of the agenda for mathematics in the 20th century, Enrico Bombieri wrote:

> The failure of the Riemann hypothesis would create havoc in the distribution of prime numbers. This fact alone singles out the Riemann hypothesis as the main open question of prime number theory.

Immediate consequences

This is easy to describe: there were none. As noted, success with the Prime Number Theorem only came some 30 years after Riemann's death with the work of Hadamard and de la Vallée-Poussin. To get that far, it was necessary to unpack a theory of the rate of growth of complex functions as the variable increases. The result can depend on the direction in which it does so. It is fair to say that almost nothing better demonstrates the depth of Riemann's insight than the silence that followed his paper for so long.

5. Minimal surfaces

It is a widespread theme in mathematics that the extreme examples of a given class of objects have special properties not always shared by every object in the same class. In particular, the path of a physical object, say a ray of light, from one specified point to another minimizes a quantity called the action, and the principle of least action has been intensively studied and used from the early 19th century to the present day. Indeed, it proved to be a formulation of classical mechanics that could be extended to quantum mechanics.

In geometry, paths of the shortest lengths joining two points are called geodesics, and surfaces of the least area spanning a given curve in space are called minimal surfaces. Minimal surfaces can be expected to have attractive properties, but it had been very difficult to describe more than a few of them until Riemann's work 1860s, as we shall now see.

The build-up

It is clear that the shortest curve joining two points in a plane is the straight line. But what is the shortest curve joining two points on a curved surface and which is constrained to lie in the surface (no bridges, no tunnels)?

On a sphere, the answer is not too difficult to see: it is the shorter of the two great circular arcs cut out on the sphere by the plane that passes through the two points and the center of the sphere. This is unique unless the two points are antipodal, like the North and South poles, in which case there are infinitely many planes of the stated kind and infinitely many curves of the required kind.

What about the curve of shortest length joining two points on some other kind of surface? Now the answer is not at all obvious.

Ancient Greek geometers had thought about this problem. It is intriguing that even in plane geometry, the shortest curve is also the straightest, and the Greeks raised the idea that the shortest curve joining two points is found by passing a rope through them and pulling it tight. We can imagine that the shortest curve on a surface is found in that way, as the curve of minimum energy in an intuitive sense.

In three-dimensional geometry, the analogous question concerned surfaces through a given closed curve, specifically this: what is the surface of least area that passes through the given curve? Of course, if the given curve lies in a plane, then the answer is obvious—it is the part of the plane that lies inside the curve. Some Greek geometers, such as Heron, had indeed thought that the plane could be defined this way, like the surface that is pulled taut as a sail (as Heath noted in his edition of Euclid's *Elements*, I, p. 171).

But what happens if the given curve is some sort of a loop in space? Remarkably, there is a simple answer. You immerse the curve in a soap solution and pull it out. The curve will be spanned by a soap film of minimum energy among all soap films that could pass through the curve, and this is a surface of least area. Intriguingly, for some curves, the soap film you get will be one of possibly several different shapes, each with a minimum area among all nearby shapes.

But even if we set aside those curves with more than one possible spanning surface of this kind, and consider those closed curves in space spanned by a unique surface of least area—a minimal surface, as such things are called—there is a downside to all this. The surfaces are found as models, but not in terms of mathematical formulae. They are often very pretty, but a soap film cannot be studied without a precise description, nor can it be taken as a model for a building, should that be desired. In 1760, Lagrange had been the first mathematician to ask for a mathematical description of a minimal surface. To his regret, he had been able to find only the plane and was therefore completely baffled.

There are, in fact, two problems. One is to find a surface with the property that if you draw a closed curve on it, then the area of the surface within that curve is less than the area of any other surface you can draw through that curve. The other problem requires the surface through a given closed curve in space that is the minimal surface for that curve. The second problem is much harder, but Lagrange could not even solve the simpler one.

The general theory of surfaces had to be developed to meet this challenge, and progress with these problems was very slow. In the 1780s, Meusnier used his theory stating that at every point on a surface there is a quadric best approximating it to argue that a minimal surface has a characteristic property—that the circles of curvature at each point have equal and opposite radii of curvature (in the language of later geometers, he claimed that a minimal surface has zero mean curvature at each point). He used this geometric insight to exhibit the first non-trivial examples: the helicoid and the catenoid.

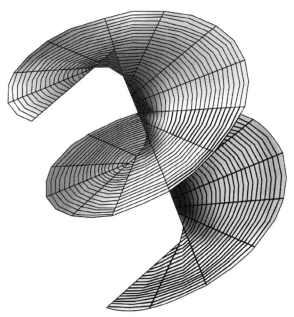

Figure 19. Part of a helicoid

The helicoid is familiar to us from spiral staircases. It is the surface swept out by a half-line fastened at its end to an axis, rising at a uniform rate and simultaneously swinging around the axis with constant angular velocity.

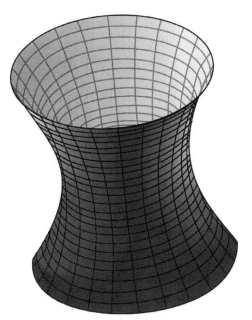

Figure 20. Part of a catenoid

The catenoid is the minimal surface spanning two circles that are of the same size and lie in two parallel planes in such a way that the line joining their centers meets each plane at right angles. It is also the surface swept out by hanging a chain that joins two corresponding points on the two circles and rotating the chain about the line joining the centers. (This curve, the catenary, is defined by the equation $y = \cosh x$.) But it only exists as a stable surface when the area of the catenoid is less than the area of the two discs that span the circles taken together.

The French mathematician Gaspard Monge who, as mentioned earlier, established the Ecole Polytechnique in Paris, continued the study of surfaces, and made a remarkable attempt at finding the general description of a minimal surface. At the end of a long and confusing chapter in a book he published in 1807 entitled *Applications d'analyse à la géométrie*, Monge came up with formulae for the x, y, and z coordinates of a minimal surface in terms of two arbitrary functions α and β.

This could have been the end of the story, or better yet, the start of a new chapter in it; instead, it was a failure. Several mathematicians pointed out that the formulae seemed to have a conspicuous failing: although the x and y coordinates would be real, the z coordinate was purely imaginary. This made no sense, and so Monge's solutions were regarded as worthless.

Curiously, not even Monge defended his results. He never explained why his critics were wrong—perhaps his long-winded arguments had confused even him. In fact, his mistake is not too difficult to remedy. It follows from the way that α and β enter the story that they are complex, but suitable combinations of them will both be real. This insight allows the formulae Monge came up with to be rewritten so that all three coordinates are real. To do so requires a cunning—but by no means deep—idea. Perhaps that was all that Monge missed, but without it, it may seem that his work had led irretrievably away from its goal.

The next minimal surfaces were found by Heinrich Scherk in 1831. The German mathematician spotted some simple solutions to the equation that Lagrange had come up with, but his approach did not lead to any general line of attack. By the middle of the 19th century, this failure to find minimal surfaces was emerging as a challenge to the mathematical community.

Among geometers, Gauss was unusual in not being interested in minimal surfaces, although he was interested in the related subject of capillarity. But his profound rewriting of differential geometry stood as a challenge to the French mathematicians in the years after Monge's death in 1818. Eventually, two of them responded: Joseph Liouville published a re-edition of Monge's book on the subject in 1850, adding an extensive 40-page appendix on Gauss's approach. At around the same time, Ossian Bonnet also published papers on every aspect of differential geometry.

In his 1848 paper entitled "Mémoire sur la théorie générale des surfaces," Bonnet used the Gauss map to obtain an image of a surface on the sphere, from which it is easy to get a map of the surface on a plane. Given such a set-up, the mathematician can ask: what properties of my original surface show up as what properties on their image in the plane? Bonnet found that when the surface has equal and opposite radii of curvature, the Gauss map is conformal, and the x, y, z coordinates of the surface can be taken to be harmonic functions. This was good enough for him, and he proclaimed he had solved the problem of minimal surfaces. In fact, he had missed the most important part.

Riemann's breakthrough

It is not clear whether Riemann knew of Bonnet's work. However, he could work it out for himself if he chose to, and on some date around 1860, he did.

He gave himself a surface and mapped it by the Gauss map to the sphere. He supposed that the surface was a least area surface, meaning that any way in which a piece of the surface is altered while the rest stays fixed, at least initially, increases the area of the surface. He then asked for the corresponding property of the Gauss map and showed that it had to be a complex analytic map.

In a sense, this is what Bonnet had shown—that the Gauss map is conformal, and there are harmonic coordinates in the story. But he had not looked to see if the Gauss map could be regarded as a complex analytic map. To Riemann, who was deeply committed to the study of complex analytic maps (which are conformal at almost every point where they are defined) and harmonic functions, it could well have seemed a natural thing to investigate.

Riemann now explored the connection between minimal surfaces and conformal Gauss maps and found that he could obtain a minimal surface for every complex analytic map (satisfying a modest technical restriction). Given any complex analytic map, he could write down the coordinate functions of a minimal surface. This really was the end of the first chapter in the study of minimal surfaces—no longer did the mathematician have to defer to the experimenter with his soap bubbles.

And by then, there really was an experimenter. The Belgian physicist Joseph Plateau was a distinguished scientist, and almost completely blind in the 1860s when he embarked on a series of experiments on soap films spanning various wire shapes (called contours or boundaries). His many papers, published in 1874 as a two-volume book, describe in careful detail numerous experiments on soap films and on liquid films floating in a different liquid of equal density, often constrained by various boundaries.

His procedure was to lead with the theory, typically an informal but mathematically aware study of mean curvatures. He compared the best mathematical theories with his observational findings, and then proceeded to novel observations by, for example, varying the initial state. Very often, his interest was in the stability of the shapes he found.

Here we should note that mathematically the study of minimal surfaces concerns a piece of surface with a fixed boundary, and looks at how the area of the surface varies with its shape. What is called the first variation of the surface is analogous to the first derivative of the area, and what we have been calling a minimal surface is one whose first variation vanishes (this is similar to the way one finds maxima and minima of a function of a single variable by finding the points where its derivative vanishes). Strictly speaking, I should have called the surfaces we are interested in 'extremal surfaces' because the first variation, in general, cannot distinguish local minima and local maxima, but of course, in the least area problem there cannot be a maximum, so only minima can occur. However, among extremal surfaces, the question of their stability arises. The stability of an extremal surface is controlled by the second variation of its area (in some sense this is the second derivative of the area as the shape is changed and the boundary held fixed). However, in the 1860s, this branch of mathematics was poorly understood. It was later to be studied thoroughly by Schwarz.

As part of his findings, Plateau also provided simple pictures to illustrate the catenoid, which he was the first to name. As he discussed, there is also an unstable catenoid that spans the circles. It lies inside the first catenoid, and, as Plateau showed, when the rings move further apart, the catenoids move together until they coincide when the distance between the rings becomes a little more than 2/3 times their diameter. Beyond that, there is no catenoid that spans the rings, and the catenoidal soap film collapses into two flat discs spanning the circles. (If you do this with real soap film, the catenoid collapses with a surprisingly audible pop.)

But Plateau had been raising the question about minimal surfaces: given a closed curve in space, find the surface of least area that passes through it. Riemann also turned to this question. This was a very hard problem, and he could only deal with the simplest cases, but we can get a glimpse of what he did by looking at a related, but simpler, problem.

This problem asks for a function that maps the unit disc onto a given triangle in the plane. As put, that's too easy: just squash the disc into shape like a piece of pastry dough. The problem, therefore, asks that the map be complex analytic, except at the points that are to map to the vertices of the triangle. It turns out that this can be done, and explicit formulae found that describe it. What about more complicated shapes? Can the disc be mapped onto a square in this fashion? The young Schwarz had taken up this problem. He intended it as a special case of the Riemann mapping theorem, which he did not believe that Riemann had adequately proved; he was very pleased when he found that it could be solved, and the solution exhibited explicitly (it involves a simple elliptic function).

What about the problem of mapping the unit disc onto an arbitrary polygon in the plane? This, too, can be done, as was shown almost simultaneously by Schwarz and Elwin Bruno Christoffel. Their success provoked a furious priority dispute—Schwarz, in particular, was very ambitious—and it seems impossible today to decide who came first. Mathematicians today speak of the Schwarz–Christoffel formula when they need to use the result.

It has an easy part—getting the angles correct—and a hard part—getting the lengths of the sides correct. That is to say that if we want to construct the map explicitly, say for a computer to be told what it is, then the exact positions of the points on the boundary of the disc that map to the vertices of the triangle can only be done approximately.

The Plateau problem is almost exactly the same, except that we are to imagine that the boundary curve is a polygonal curve in space—a curve that is made up of a number of straight edges joined at various points.

The mathematical argument that leads to the Schwarz-Christoffel formula involves an unknown function, leading to a differential equation that the unknown function must satisfy. This differential equation is a linear first-order equation, and such equations are easy to solve. A very similar argument for the polygonal Plateau problem involves two unknown functions, bringing about a linear second-order equation, and it too is easy to solve. However, the solution now must fit the specifics of the problem, and that is a much harder problem than before.

Riemann could solve it in a few simple cases, and he could show that in every case, there were as many unknown constants in the solution functions as there were constraints imposed by choice of a polygon. That doesn't prove that the problem can be solved in every case, but at least it doesn't rule it out.

Among the problems that Riemann solved explicitly was that of a regular four-sided polygonal curve in space. Another was a generalization of the catenoid, first to two off-center circles in parallel planes, and then to a finite number of circles in parallel planes (called the Riemann staircase).

Riemann did not publish this work. It seems to have been one of several topics he was working on in the early 1860s, but the collapse of his health prevented him from finishing them.

He had asked some of his former students to write up what they could from his papers, and the mathematical community supported this endeavor. It fell to Hattendorff to deal with the drafts on minimal surfaces, and he put something together for the Göttingen journal that carried several of Riemann's posthumous papers. He remarked, in effect, that the formulae in the paper were Riemann's, but the words were his own. This provoked a response from Schwarz and his mentor, Weierstrass, in Berlin. Back in 1860, Weierstrass had found a way to parameterize a surface with equal and opposite radii of curvature, and it had led him to realize that (almost) every complex analytic function gave rise to a minimal surface. This incited Schwarz to take up the Plateau problem, and one of his earliest successes was solving it for a polygonal contour composed of four of the six sides of a regular tetrahedron (so it has four equal sides meeting at angles of $\pi/3$). Weierstrass had then claimed that the methods he and Schwarz were using could solve the Plateau problem for any polygonal contour, although no details were given.

When they learned of what Riemann had done, and Schwarz was one of those who advised on editing the manuscripts, they began dating their own publications with unusual precision, suggesting that Hattendorff could have written his words only after learning of their work. Quite possibly what irked Schwarz, in particular, was that Riemann had already solved the Plateau problem for a regular four-sided polygonal curve in space, and he (Schwarz) had just won a prize for a paper in which he too dealt only with the regular case—but that is a matter of speculation.

Be that as it may, and there is no reason to accept the accusation, there is little excuse for Schwarz and Weierstrass to continue to claim, as they did in the 1880s (see Schwarz 1885), that the problem was solved apart from some straight-forward work needed to resolve it explicitly.

Riemann's own work made that claim look implausible, and they never delivered a detailed account. That was left to the French mathematical Gaston Darboux, who wrote the matter up at length in the second volume of his *Théorie des Surfaces* in 1893.

6. Real functions

A function in mathematics describes how some variables depend on others: how the speed of a falling body depends on the time it has been falling, how people's blood sugar levels depend on their diet. Functions describe many aspects of our lives. The general idea was introduced into mathematics by Euler in the 1740s when he rewrote the calculus of Newton and Leibniz in the language of functions, and it has been central to mathematics ever since. But only with the work of Cauchy in the 1820s did the full generality of the concept become apparent, and the need to describe arbitrary functions force itself upon mathematicians' attention. At the same time, such functions came into mathematics with the work of Joseph Fourier on heat propagation, but Fourier's approach was far from rigorous, and attempts to understand it were to lead Riemann to discover functions that seemed to defy the calculus altogether.

Fourier series

Joseph Fourier's 1822 book, *Théorie Analytique de la Chaleur* (*The Analytical Theory of Heat*), on the propagation of heat in solids, is one of the most important contributions ever made to the theories of both pure and applied mathematics. In it, he derived a differential equation (the heat equation) governing the flow of heat, and then showed how to solve it in numerous cases in which the shape and temperature on the boundary did not make the task too complicated.

Fourier said only a little about what heat is, and how different bodies have different specific heats. His equation, however, was new and convincing, although the methods by which it was solved left much to be desired. Indeed, the book's contributions to pure mathematics was the idea that functions could be represented in a particular way, as well as the challenge to vindicate this idea.

Fourier claimed that any function defined on an interval such as $[0, 2\pi]$ could be represented as an infinite series of sines and/or cosines, and thus be extended to a periodic function on the entire real line. It was easy to show that functions written in this way would formally solve the heat equation (it would still have to be shown that the series converged). The problems lay with the representation of a given function: in determining the coefficients in the infinite series and in showing that the series so obtained equaled the given function. Fourier had no doubts about his method on either count. It turned out that he was right regarding a wide range of functions, but neither claim was true in complete generality.

We can do well with the example of Fourier sine series. These are series of the form

$$\frac{1}{2}a_0 + a_1 \sin x + a_2 \sin 2x + \cdots + a_n \sin nx + \cdots .$$

Fourier claimed that given any function $f(x)$ defined on an interval such as $[0, 2\pi]$ one could write

$$f(x) = \frac{1}{2}a_0 + a_1 \sin x + a_2 \sin 2x + \cdots + a_n \sin nx + \cdots ,$$

where

$$a_n = \frac{1}{2\pi} \int_0^{2\pi} f(x) \sin nx\, dx.$$

This is because

$$\int_0^{2\pi} \sin kx \sin nx\, dx = \begin{cases} 0 & \text{when} \quad k \neq n, \quad \text{and} \\ \pi & \text{when} \quad k = n. \end{cases}$$

For example, the Fourier series for the function $f(x) = x$ on the interval from $-\pi$ to π comes out as

$$2\left(\sin x - \frac{1}{2}\sin 2x + \frac{1}{3}\sin 3x - \cdots\right).$$

Figure 21 shows the sum of the first 100 terms in the series.

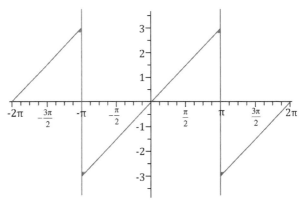

Figure 21. The first 100 terms of the Fourier series for
$f(x) = x$

Fourier demonstrated that the series for the function
$F(x) = \pm\pi/4$ is

$$\cos(x) - \frac{1}{3}\cos(3x) + \frac{1}{5}\cos(5x) - \frac{1}{7}\cos(7x) + \cdots.$$

Figure 22 shows the sum of the first 100 terms in the series.

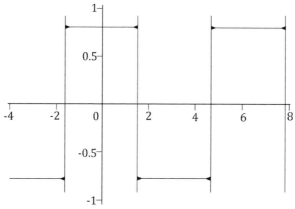

Figure 22. *The first 100 terms of the Fourier series for*
$F(x) = \pm\pi/4$

Fourier indeed claimed that any function $f(x)$ defined on $[0, 2\pi]$ may be developed in this way, and that the resulting series converges; moreover, he argued that for every value of x in $[0, 2\pi]$ the series equals the corresponding value of $f(x)$. This claim was quickly challenged by several mathematicians, including Cauchy, who tried and failed to prove it. The first mathematician to defend him successfully was Dirichlet, who knew Fourier personally and had benefitted from his acquaintance with him when he went to Paris in 1822.

Dirichlet, however, could not prove Fourier's claim in general. He could prove it only for a function that is continuous and monotonic (non-decreasing or non-increasing) on an interval, and for a function that is made up of finitely many such functions, each of which is defined on an interval and the intervals are joined together at their endpoints (such as the function with the graph shown in Figure 23). If the function had jumps where the intervals are joined—because the values of the two components of the function do not agree—then Dirichlet showed that the value of the Fourier series at that point was the average of the value of the function at the two endpoints.

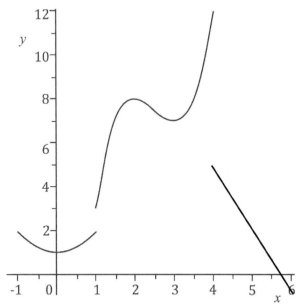

Figure 23. *The function is continuous and monotonic on the intervals* $(-1, 0), (0, 1), (1, 2), (2, 3), (3, 4),$ *and* $(4, 6)$

Dirichlet seems to have felt that these restrictions were only temporary expedients and that they would be lifted when a better proof was found. But he was completely clear that Fourier's method of evaluating the Fourier coefficients was far from general because it supposed that the integral

$$\frac{1}{2\pi} \int_0^{2\pi} f(x) \sin nx \, dx$$

made sense for every function f. For this to be the case, the function f would have to be integrable, and Dirichlet gave an example of a function that was not. It is the function that takes one value b when x is rational, and a different value c when x is irrational.

What should we make of such a bizarre function? It looks as if it has been brought in to make a point, as if it is one of those irritating things that only pedants could like, and perhaps that is what Dirichlet initially thought of it. But if so, then by the time he was advising Riemann on the subject, his viewpoint had shifted markedly. The very reach of the calculus was at stake: could the calculus, the greatest breakthrough in mathematics since the time of the Greeks, have significant limitations, and were they being reached?

To over-simplify, but not by much, when Newton and Leibniz created the calculus in their two rather different ways, they imagined that it applied to every curve. Euler, when he shifted the foundational weight from curves to functions, thought much the same. Everyone knew there were exceptions: the function $y = |x|$ has a sharp point at the origin and cannot be differentiable there, but that did not dent confidence in the calculus.

Cauchy changed this opinion in the 1820s, in the books that came out of his lecture courses at the Ecole Polytechnique, and his work met with considerable hostility. He shifted attention to what it is for a function to be continuous, rather than assuming that functions were almost always differentiable. He proved that a continuous function is integrable and investigated when some kinds of discontinuous functions are also integrable. He gave precise conditions for a function to be differentiable, showing that continuous functions need not be differentiable. And he also demonstrated that the so-called Fundamental Theorem of the Calculus holds: if we integrate a function and differentiate the result, we obtain the original function.

Cauchy was not immune to mistakes. In many ways, Dirichlet was his natural successor and was certainly the man who brought Cauchy's high standards for mathematical rigor to Germany. His investigation of the convergence of the Fourier series is a major example of how he spread the novel methods. It is precisely because Cauchy's work made it necessary to talk of functions being integrable and differentiable—with the implication that a given function may not be—that allowed Dirichlet to wonder what could be said mathematically about functions that may not be continuous, or even integrable.

The problem is that without a collection of good examples, it is not clear what can be said, and Riemann's contribution here was to find a way of constructing just such examples.

The saw-tooth function

Just as an explorer must defend his or her claim that there is gold in those hills by going there and bringing the gold back, so a mathematician must not only say that there are functions with novel properties, but he or she must then exhibit such a function and prove that it has the stated properties. This is particularly difficult when the properties are thought to be contrary to all experience.

Riemann admitted that functions that are not continuous and monotonic, at least in pieces, are unlikely to occur in nature. The reasons for studying them were drawn instead from mathematics itself. He noted that Dirichlet had already commented as follows:

> The topic has a very close connection with the principles of infinitesimal calculus, and can serve to bring greater clarity and rigour to these principles,

and Riemann added that these strange functions were beginning to turn up in pure mathematics, including number theory.

Riemann began by observing (1867a, § 6) that "since these functions have never been considered before, it will be good to give a definite example." His example was of a function that, like Dirichlet's example of a non-integrable function, had infinitely many points of discontinuity, but which, unlike Dirichlet's, was integrable.

His example was a function with infinitely many jumps in any interval, but for which most of the jumps are arbitrarily small (which is how the function can be integrable).

First he introduced a function $r(x)$ with a saw-tooth graph, as in Figure 24 (but the verticals are incorrect mathematically; in fact, the function has a jump discontinuity at those points). It has a slope of 1, its values go from $-\frac{1}{2}$ to $\frac{1}{2}$, and it jumps at the points

$$x = \ldots, -\frac{3}{2}, -\frac{1}{2}, \frac{1}{2}, \frac{3}{2}, \ldots$$

which are called the half-integer points.

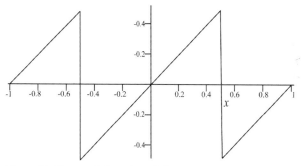

Figure 24. Riemann's function $r(x)$

Then he tweaked the definition to produce a new function with twice the slope of the original one and twice as many points where it jumps, and tweaked it again to produce a new function with four times the original slope and four times as many points where it jumps, and so on. Then he added these functions all together, multiplying each successive contribution by a factor so that the sum converged. This produced the function

$$R(x) = r(x) + \frac{r(2x)}{2^2} + \ldots + \frac{r(nx)}{n^2} + \ldots.$$

Of course, we can only draw approximations to Riemann's function $R(x)$ that take account of the first so many terms; Figure 25 shows the sum of the first 14 terms of the function.

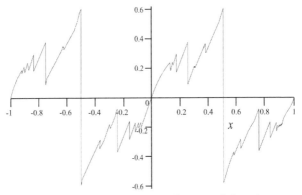

Figure 25. The first fourteen terms of Riemann's function
$R(x)$

The hard work was to show that the function does indeed have infinitely many points where it jumps and nothing is smoothed out or patched over as more and more terms are added together. Some more detail will be found in the section 'More about the Mathematics' at the end of the chapter. Then it has to be shown that the resulting function is integrable.

Riemann's definition of an integrable function is essentially a more careful version of Cauchy's. Given a function defined on an interval, the area under its graph is approximated by rectangular strips erected on the given interval, and the height of each strip is chosen to lie between the heights of the vertical edges of the strip. The value of the area is approximated by the sum of the areas of the strips. As the number of strips increases without limit, the question is whether the sum tends to a finite limit. If it does, irrespective of how the strips have been chosen, the limiting value is the area under the graph of the function, and the function is said to be integrable.

Now, the area under the graph of the function can be thought of as being the product of the width of the whole interval and the average value of the function. Riemann posited that if a function remains integrable as the right-hand edge of the strip is moved, then the integral is a function of the right-hand end point; one can readily agree that this average value should not be affected either by a finite number of jumps in the value of the function, or by it oscillating within certain limits. Riemann's function has infinitely many jumps, but only a finite number are above a certain size, and so there is an average value of the function and it is therefore integrable.

Trigonometric series

To obtain a variety of examples of these novel functions, but about which something could nonetheless be said, Riemann had the idea of writing down an expression of roughly the right kind. This is what is today called a trigonometric series,

(1) $\quad \Omega(x) = A_0 + A_1(x) + A_2(x) + \ldots + A_n(x) + \ldots,$

where

$$A_0 = a_0/2, A_n(x) = a_n \cos nx + b_n \sin nx.$$

He assumed that the sequence of functions $A_n(x)$ gets steadily smaller and converges to zero for each value of x.

He then wrote down the series that is obtained by integrating each term formally twice:

$$F(x) = C + C'x + A_0 x^2/2 - \sum_n \frac{A_n(x)}{n^2}$$

(2)

Because the sequence of functions $A_n(x)$ becomes arbitrarily small, all but the first so many terms must be less than 1 for all values of x. As soon as $A_n(x)$ becomes less than 1, the infinite sum converges. Therefore, the series for $F(x)$ converges for every value of x, and Riemann showed it defined a continuous function of x.

This well-behaved function $F(x)$ remembers its origins, in the sense that its second derivative

$$\mathcal{D}^2 F(x) :=$$

(3)

$$\lim_{\alpha,\beta \to 0} \frac{F(x + \alpha + \beta) - F(x + \alpha - \beta) - F(x - \alpha + \beta) + F(x - \alpha - \beta)}{4\alpha\beta}$$

exists and equals $\Omega(x)$ whenever Ω converges. After some delicate analysis, Riemann proved a lemma, enabling him to conclude that a function f can be represented on $[0, 2\pi]$ by a Fourier series everywhere that the Fourier series converges, if and only there is a continuous function F that satisfies both the above condition on the second derivative and another condition (too technical to state here) that prevents the function from oscillating too wildly.

Riemann's arguments were difficult and not convincing. The English mathematician Henry John Stephen Smith and the German Paul du Bois-Reymond denied that Riemann's conditions were sufficient. In fact, they are correct.

Riemann now gave a range of examples of new and unexpected phenomena. Most of them required careful examination before his claims about them could be confirmed, and this confirmation required some agility with integrals. But Dirichlet had shown that a well-behaved function (one that is continuous and piecewise monotonic on a finite collection of intervals) is equal to its Fourier series, except where it jumps. This leaves open the cases where the given function is not integrable, so the Fourier coefficients cannot be found, and the cases where the Fourier series can be found but the function is not piecewise continuous or not piecewise monotonic. In these cases, it was not known if these functions are equal to their Fourier series representations. There is also the question of what can be said about a function defined by a trigonometric series that is not also a Fourier series—functions that cannot be represented as Fourier series.

If a function is not piecewise continuous, it will have infinitely many jumps in an interval. If it is not piecewise monotonic, then it will have infinitely many maxima and minima in an interval. An example of such a function is the function $f(x)$ that is defined as follows: $f(x) = x\sin(1/x)$ when $x \neq 0$ and $f(0) = 0$ (see Figure 26).

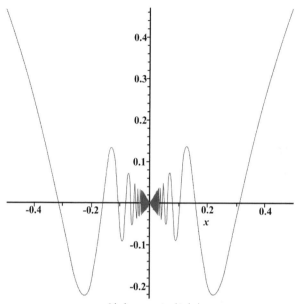

Figure 26. A graph of $f(x) = x\sin(1/x)$

Riemann found functions with infinitely many maxima and minima that are integrable without being representable by a Fourier series. For example,

$$\frac{d(x^{\nu}\cos(1/x))}{dx}$$

on $0 < x \leq 2\pi$, with $0 < \nu < 1/2$. The function is integrable, but it is possible to find a sequence of values of the variable x on which the function increases indefinitely and another sequence of values of the variable x on which the function decreases indefinitely. These values interlace—between two adjacent ones of one kind is one of the other kind—and they get closer together; thus, the function is oscillating more and more. For this reason, it fails to have a Fourier series—the Fourier integrals for the coefficients do not converge. Conversely, there are functions that cannot be integrated but can be represented by a trigonometric series. For example, the function

$$\sum_{k=1}^{\infty} \frac{r(kx)}{k}$$

exists for every rational value of x and is representable, but series is not bounded in any interval, no matter how small, and consequently is not integrable.

Another example is
$$\Sigma c_n \cos n^2 x,$$

where $c_n \to 0$ but $\Sigma c_n = \infty$. As Riemann explained:

" . . . if $x/2\pi$ is rational with denominator m in lowest terms, then clearly the series either converges or diverges to infinity according as

$$\sum_{n=0}^{m-1} \cos n^2 x , \quad \sum_{n=0}^{m-1} \sin n^2 x$$

are zero or not. Both cases arise, by a well-known theorem on partitioning the circle, for infinitely many values of m between any two bounds, no matter how close."

Next, he exhibited trigonometric series that converge, although the series obtained from them by term-by-term integration is not integrable on any interval, however small. Finally, he showed that a trigonometric series can converge for infinitely many points in any interval, and yet the coefficients do not tend to zero. For example,

$$\Sigma \sin(n!\pi x),$$

which converges not only for every rational value of x but also for some irrational numbers, such as $\sin 1$ and its multiples, etc.

Immediate consequences

The consequences of Riemann's paper were momentous. Once published, it became impossible for mathematicians to pretend that they understood the functions defined by Fourier series representations, or that there was not a teeming collection of functions with unexpected properties. Their study was taken up in several countries under the name of "assumptionless" functions, meaning functions with no particular properties at all.

To give just one example, it was soon shown that there are functions that behave like $x\sin(1/x)$
at every rational point in the interval $[-1, 1]$.

The existence of functions that are continuous but not differentiable or, worse, so badly discontinuous that they are not even integrable posed a fundamental challenge to the range, scope, and correctness of the calculus that it was to take the work of two generations of mathematicians to overcome. Indeed, some of the deepest problems in mathematics to this day, for example in the broad topic of probability, involve the sorts of functions whose existence Riemann was the first to explore.

More about the Mathematics

Recall that Riemann's saw-tooth function $r(x)$ is defined as follows: for each real number x that is not of the form $n + \frac{1}{2}$, where n is an integer,

$$r(x) = x - m(x)$$

where $m(x)$ is the integer such that $|x - m(x)|$ is a minimum. When x is of the form $n + \frac{1}{2}$, $m(x)$ is not defined—it might be either n or $n + 1$—and Riemann set

$$r(x) = 0.$$

The values of this function $r(x)$ lie strictly between $-\frac{1}{2}$ and $\frac{1}{2}$, it is zero where x is either an integer or an integer plus a half, its graph is made up of line segments of slope 1 and jumps at the half-integer points

$$x = \ldots, -\frac{3}{2}, -\frac{1}{2}, \frac{1}{2}, \frac{3}{2}, \ldots$$

The function $R(x)$ is defined as follows:

$$R(x) = r(x) + \frac{r(2x)}{2^2} + \ldots + \frac{r(nx)}{n^2} + \ldots.$$

This series converges, because every term in it is less than the corresponding term of a famous convergent series:

$$\left| \frac{r(nx)}{n^2} \right| < \frac{1}{2n^2},$$

and Euler had shown that

$$1 + \frac{1}{4} + \frac{1}{9} + \cdots + \frac{1}{n^2} + \cdots = \frac{\pi^2}{6}.$$

So for all x, $f(x) < \frac{\pi^2}{12}$.

The function $r(nx)$ is made up of line segments of slope n, jumping at the points where nx is a half-integer or x is an integer divided by $2n$ and so x is of the form $m/2n$ where m is an integer.

As a result, the function is discontinuous at every point $x = m/2n$ where m and $2n$ are relatively prime.

Now, any interval of real numbers, however small, contains points of this kind. To see this, consider an arbitrary interval (a, b). It is of length $b - a$. Now whenever $n > \frac{1}{2(b-a)}$ we have $\frac{1}{2n} < b - a$. Consider the numbers $\frac{m}{2n}$ as m runs through the integers. These numbers increase in steps of $\frac{1}{2n}$, which is less than $b - a$, so at least one of them must fall into the interval we are contemplating. Therefore, every interval contains a number of the form $m/2n$, because a and b were chosen arbitrarily.

We can also see how big the jumps are at these points. At the point $x = \frac{p}{2n}$, the right- and left-hand limits of the function f are

$$f(x+) = f(x) - \frac{1}{2n^2} \left(\sum_k \frac{1}{(2k+1)^2} \right) = f(x) - \frac{\pi^2}{16n^2}$$

and

$$f(x-) = f(x) + \frac{1}{2n^2} \left(\sum_k \frac{1}{(2k+1)^2} \right) = f(x) + \frac{\pi^2}{16n^2}.$$

Nonetheless, the function f is integrable, because the contribution of jumps, $\pi^2/8n^2$, exceeds a given bound at only finitely many points.

7. And another thing . . .

It is impossible to describe all of Riemann's accomplishments, so here is just a glimpse of what is NOT included in this book.

Most interesting problems in mathematical accounts of the natural world involve more than one independent variable, and even position in space requires three coordinates. The differential equations that go with these functions are called partial differential equations, and their study goes back to the 1740s and the work of d'Alembert, Euler, and others. But Cauchy was the first to apply, around 1820, rigorous methods sensitive to the subtleties of these equations. Dirichlet's lectures in the 1850s did this as well.

Riemann contributed significantly to the analysis of the transmission of sound—he was the first to describe compression waves, rarefaction, and the existence of shock waves. With an important correction to the underlying physics—Riemann's analysis did not consider the conservation of energy—his paper became a model for investigations into a whole class of partial differential equations.

In the field of ordinary differential equations, he was the first to show that linear equations can have solutions that only become infinite where one or more of the coefficients of the equation become infinite. A significant example of this was an equation already studied by Gauss, the so-called hypergeometric equation, which plays a major role in the study of elliptic functions. These equations have significant geometrical implications, and a generation later, one of Henri Poincaré's first important discoveries was their close ties to non-Euclidean geometry. In unpublished lectures, Riemann had extended these ideas to other classes of ordinary differential equations.

He also made innovative use of the technical aspects of the study of elliptic functions and Abelian functions to parametrize algebraic curves and discuss their symmetries, and from the same body of work, he found examples of functions on the borderline between continuous and differentiable.

However, Riemann's contributions to theoretical physics were not lasting. But his ideas about geometry were to change both mathematics and physics forever.

8. Riemann's Legacy

R iemann changed mathematics completely by making it a much more conceptual activity, one less driven by agility with complicated formulae. This movement had its roots in Gauss's work. It also derived from the work of Évariste Galois in algebra that went in directions that Riemann did not consider. Still, many of them were pioneered by his old friend Dedekind, who explicitly drew his inspiration from Riemann.

Conceptual arguments have two virtues: they deepen understanding by providing better causal chains, and they help make precise what one should try to prove and to calculate.

There are many occasions in mathematics where an argument works because some number turns out to be zero, or less than 2, say. Often this is shown for the first time by a brute force calculation, leaving the mathematician with an unsatisfactory proof. The number has this crucial value because it does, not for any other reason, and we do not understand why it could not have had a different value.

For example, Abel had shown that in the study of what today we call Abelian integrals, an integer p turns up and plays a crucial role. These integrals involve a polynomial $g(x, y)$ in two complex variables, and this polynomial determines the number p—but in a complicated way. Riemann showed that the number p has a natural geometrical meaning that relates directly to the problem at hand; it is the topological genus of the surface with equation $g(x, y) = 0$ indicating the most basic properties of the surface and of the corresponding polynomial. Calculating the number p in any given case is still necessary, and not easier, but the implications of its taking this value or that are much easier to understand. Thus, given a specific polynomial, the first thing a mathematician now knows to do is to calculate the genus p.

Another example is the close connection that Riemann discovered between complex and harmonic functions. Harmonic functions were already well understood, and their properties could now be seen to determine key properties of complex functions. This gave Riemann a precise way to single out the maps from $\mathbb{R}^2$ to $\mathbb{R}^2$ that are complex differentiable maps from $\mathbb{C}$ to $\mathbb{C}$—they must be harmonic and conformal except where the derivative vanishes.

This does not mean that agility with formulae could be forgotten. On the contrary, like all the best mathematicians, Riemann could calculate whatever he needed, provided it could be done at all. There have been numerous occasions where calculation played an essential role that I have had to conceal. Riemann's work displays, for example, lengthy calculations of curvature in manifolds of dimension greater than 2, and difficult manipulation of formulae in the study of the zeta function and trigonometric series.

Einstein and geometry

When Einstein was a student at the ETH in Zürich around 1900, he had little time for mathematics, which he regarded firmly as a tool for physics of little other value. He was still of this opinion when he wrote the three papers in 1905 that made him famous—on the photoelectric effect, Brownian motion, and the special theory of relativity. He saw that it was necessary to rethink how we talk about space and time when we are converting the observations of one observer to another moving at high relative velocities, but he did not see any value in recasting the theory geometrically. For him, the important conceptual issues were in physics; mathematics was mere algebra. Thus, he was unimpressed when, in 1908, Hermann Minkowski re-presented his theory as a theory of four-dimensional space-time.

But by then, Einstein had already come to what he later called his "happiest" realization: that gravitation and acceleration are different ways of looking at the same thing, and therefore equivalent.

He argued that the following two situations are equivalent: in the first, he is sitting at rest, and a window cleaner falls past his window. In the second, he is accelerating in a rocket, and there is an astronaut at rest outside his window. This does not say that he and the window cleaner are equivalent, only that any analysis of the window cleaner's fall in a gravitational field is equivalent to an analysis of someone at rest, as seen in an accelerating frame of reference.

Now, when Einstein's thoughts turned to understanding gravity, he found that he was thinking of how its effects were manifested geometrically. This was particularly clear when he looked at a gravitational field that varies from point to point.

He supposed that there was a two-dimensional space that took the form of a disc rotating about its center with constant angular velocity ω. On such a disc, all its points go round in circles, and they are accelerating because they are changing their direction all the time.

Moreover, points in the disc are also moving faster and accelerating more, the farther away from the center they are, and every point is moving at any instant in a direction perpendicular to the radius of the disc through that point.

By the equivalence, Einstein was hoping to establish between theories of acceleration and theories of gravity, allowing him to think of the rotating disc as displaying the effects of gravity.

What we make of the geometry on the disc is determined by where we are. Suppose that Jill is at the center of the disc and rotating with it. Objects in the disc retain their relative positions relative to her; everything for her is the same as if she were at rest on a stationary disc, and she says that the geometry is Euclidean.

Suppose now that she spreads a spider's web of rods across the disc, along the radii and at right angles to the radii, all of them of equal length ℓ, where ℓ is very small when compared to the size of the disc. By first counting rods along a radius from the center, and then by counting the rods that lie along the corresponding circle, she can confirm that the radius of the circle of radius r is $2\pi r$. For example, if she places 955 of the rods along a radius, she will find that almost exactly 6000 rods lie along the corresponding circle C, giving her a value for π as it turns out, of 3.1414. She will always find that whatever radius she uses, the ratio of circumference to radius comes out at very much this value for π.

But what does Jack, who sits just above the center of the disc and is not rotating with it, see? What does he say is the geometry of the disc? One of Einstein's fundamental discoveries in his special theory of relativity is that an observer sees a moving object as contracted along its direction of motion by an amount that depends on the relative velocity of object and observer. An object moving with velocity $v = \omega r$ relative to an observer seems to that observer to have its length contracted by a factor of $\sqrt{1 - v^2}$. Therefore, measuring rods on the rotating disc that point along the direction of motion, seem to Jack to be of different lengths than rods that are not moving in that direction; moreover, the ones farther out are going faster and so appear shorter than the ones nearer in. But the rods placed along the radii are not moving in the radial direction at all; their lengths appear to him to be unaltered (that is, the same length as Jill says they are).

So, when Jack looks at Jill's spider's web of rods, he does not see equal rods in each of the radial and tangential directions. He agrees, of course, that there are 955 rods along a radius, and 6000 rods along the corresponding circumference. He also agrees that all the radial rods and all the tangential rods are of the same length. But he disputes that the radial rods are the same length as the tangential rods. If he asks Jill to take rod 955, which has one end P on the circle C and points outward, and rotate it through a right angle until it points along the circle C, he does not see that it keeps the same length. Instead, he sees it steadily shrink. If, for example, at this point of the disc, the velocity is $v = 4/5$, then $\sqrt{1 - v^2} = 3/5$, and he sees that the tangential rod's length is only $3/5$ of the radial rod. What Jill sees as a small disc center P, Jack sees as an ellipse, much longer along the radial than the tangential direction.

Now, Jack and Jill will always agree that if the radius is measured by rods of length n_r and the circle C is measured by n_t rods of length ℓ_t then the ratio of circumference to radius is

$$\frac{n_t \ell_t}{n_r \ell_r}.$$

If Jill says that $\ell_r = \ell_t$ then this ratio is simply $\frac{n_t}{n_r}$, and in the case under consideration this ratio is 3.1414. Jack agrees that, but he does not agree that $\ell_r = \ell_t$. He insists that

$$\ell_t = \frac{\ell_r}{\sqrt{1 - v^2}},$$

and so, he measures the ratio of circumference to radius to be

$$\frac{n_t \ell_t}{n_r \ell_r} = \frac{n_t}{n_r} \frac{1}{\sqrt{1 - v^2}},$$

which with the given velocity is $3.1414 \times 5/3$.

To see that this is correct, note that if Jack measures the small moving disc to be a circle, and so says $\ell_t = \ell_r$, then Jill must have produced an ellipse much longer along the radial than the tangential direction. Jack will say that the circumference is longer than Euclidean geometry demands. The geometry he sees on the disc is some sort of non-Euclidean geometry.

Einstein concluded from arguments such as these that forces—gravity, for instance—may be understood by saying that space is deformed, and is no longer Euclidean. But he realized that to make progress, he had to take mathematics seriously. Luckily for him, an old friend from his student days, Marcel Grossmann, was now a colleague on the staff at the ETH, where Einstein was a professor. Grossman had taken notes of the mathematics courses they had attended and knew what Einstein needed. Together they worked through the ideas of Gregorio Ricci and Tullio Levi-Civita, coming up with the first papers on the general theory of relativity. In this way, they showed that Riemann's ideas about geometry, grafted on to a setting in which the simplest geometry was that of

Minkowski space-time, could be made to yield the first new theory of gravity since the time of Newton.

As Einstein said of Gauss and Riemann (Einstein, 1916 and 1952, 88):

> Gauss indicated the principles according to which we can treat the geometrical relationships in the surface, and thus pointed out the way to the method of Riemann of treating multi-dimensional, non-Euclidean continua. Thus it is that mathematicians long ago solved the formal problems to which we are led by the general postulate of relativity.

Complex functions

The theory of complex functions of a complex variable grew in the 19th century from nothing to one of the most important domains. It was largely the creation of three people: Cauchy, Riemann, and Weierstrass. Much of what they did overlapped, and much of what their successors did, produced one theory out of these competing versions. When that was done, the crucial and most original contributions of Riemann's were the intimate link between complex functions and harmonic functions, and the idea of a Riemann surface.

As we saw above, the equation $w^2 = 1 - z^4$ between two complex variables defines a surface. We saw this by observing that for each value of z there will be two values of w unless $z = 1, -1, i$, or $-i$, in which case there is only one corresponding value of w. This allows us to pick one value of w for a given value of z, and to track it as z varies, thus studying functions on the surface and their integrals. This was the key that unlocked the geometrical study of elliptic and Abelian functions, although it had to be admitted that it was difficult to move the surface out of its four-dimensional home into a three-dimensional one where it can literally be seen.

Riemann's presentation of these ideas was his usual mixture of profound and naive, and it took work of two generations to fit it rigorously to the advancing theory of complex functions. The final advance was made by Hermann Weyl, one of the great mathematicians of the 20th century, in one of his best books, *The Idea of a Riemann Surface* (1913).

Riemann surfaces come in three types if they are compact, which the ones that arise from polynomial equations are: they may be a sphere, a torus, or something else. As put, this is no classification at all. What is much better—and much harder to prove—is that every Riemann surface can be obtained from precisely one of three surfaces by the process of cutting out a polygonal piece and gluing together its edges in pairs.

The first of these surfaces is the sphere. Here, the cutting and gluing process can only produce another sphere. The second of these surfaces is the plane. If we divide the plane up into equal squares, so that it looks like an infinite chessboard, and we cut out one of the squares, then we may glue together its upper and lower edges, and its left and right edges, and form a torus. If we use parallelograms instead of squares, we can get all the different kinds of torus that a complex analyst can tell apart.

The third and final one of these surfaces is the non-Euclidean disc. All the other Riemann surfaces of genus greater than 1 come about by taking the non-Euclidean disc, dividing it up into congruent polygons with the right sorts and numbers of edges, and gluing their edges together in pairs (For example, a two-holed torus is obtained from a non-Euclidean octagon with vertical angles of $\pi/4$. To obtain a torus with n holes, use a polygon with $4n$ sides and angles all of the size of $\pi/(2n)$.) This astonishing result is called the uniformization theorem. It was conjectured independently by Felix Klein and Henri Poincaré in 1881-82 and proved independently by Poincaré and Paul Koebe in 1907.

This means that a small piece of any Riemann surface is indistinguishable from the sphere, the Euclidean plane, or the non-Euclidean disc, and so the study of Riemann surfaces, and therefore a large amount of complex function theory, can be carried out with the help of geometry.

This theorem moved Weyl to exclaim (1913, vi):

> We enter the temple in which the divinity (if I may use this image) returns to itself from the earthly custody of its individual realisations: the original image of the Riemann surface itself will appear (so far as that is possible) pure and freed of all obscurities and accidents in the symbol of the two-dimensional non-Euclidean crystal.

The study of complex functions of several variables arises for many reasons, but it has a well-deserved reputation for difficulty. Weierstrass made it his life's work to penetrate it and made some progress. Poincaré achieved more by exploiting the connection with harmonic functions that Riemann had opened up. But in the new setting, the connection is looser; the analogues of the Cauchy-Riemann equations make it plain that there are harmonic functions of two or more variables that satisfy some given boundary conditions but are not the real or imaginary part of a holomorphic function because they do not satisfy all the equations.

The study of algebraic equations in several complex variables leads to the natural generalization of Riemann surfaces to higher dimensions, which are called complex manifolds. In 1941, the British mathematician W.D.V. Hodge showed that the study of these manifolds is greatly advanced by bringing together the sorts of ideas of topology and harmonic function theory that Riemann had used. The resulting Hodge theory provides a rich set of insights into the structure of these manifolds, and it has generated a further set of questions that are judged so difficult, and so important, that they form the subject of one of the prizes from Clay Mathematics Institute.

Index theorems:

Riemann's deep insight that the number of linearly independent analytic integrals on a Riemann surface is equal to the topological genus of the surface is the prototypical index theorem. It is an index theorem because it equates a number defined analytically (the number of independent integrals) with a number defined topologically (the genus). This is not only interesting, but also instructive: it grounds the analytical side of the story in something more fundamental—topology.

There are many occasions in mathematics when index theorems arise. To give just two examples, the Laplace operator in mathematical physics is fundamental to the study of potential theory, which includes the study of gravitation, electricity, and magnetism. It also plays a major role in the study of heat diffusion, and it has numerous applications of current interest in other fields. It, too, obeys an index theorem, as does the Dirac operator, which is central in relativistic physics.

Prime numbers

Analytic number theory—the use of the calculus to find out results about the integers—was largely created by Euler, Dirichlet, and Riemann. Riemann's most famous contribution, the Riemann hypothesis, remains unproven to this day, but progress has been made in other related areas.

As was said above, the prime number theorem was proved in 1896. But it provides a relatively crude estimate of the number of prime numbers less than a given number, and the Riemann hypothesis, if proven, would provide possibly the best simple estimate. So, should we expect that it is true?

Without a proof, either way, answers, even from experts, say something about the speaker as well as the state of play. There have always been mathematicians who believe the hypothesis is false; J.E. Littlewood, the distinguished British number theorist in the early decades of the 20th century, thought there was no such evidence at all. His reason was that any amount of confirmation for the first, however many zeros of the zeta function only establishes something about a finite subset of an infinite set—trouble may still lie ahead—and he knew of plausible conjectures where the first counterexample was greater than 10^{23}.

More worryingly, there are factors affecting the behavior of the zeta function that are of the order of $\log \log x$ (let us use logarithms to the base 10 rather than natural logarithms for a moment, nothing significant changes). To get a sense of how big x has to be for $\log \log x$ to have any significant size, say 6, observe that if x is a million, $x = 10^6$, then $\log x = 6$. So, for $\log \log x = 6$ we must have $\log x = 10^6$ and so $x = 10^{10^6}$, a number with a million zeros. Such numbers are beyond even the biggest modern computers.

On the other hand, it is possible to make selective searches, and in 2001 Andrew Odlyzko showed that the Riemann hypothesis is true for 10 billion zeros near zero number 10^{22}. He also referred to other authors, who have shown that the first 1.5×10^9 non-trivial zeros lie on the critical line.

Likewise, there are ways of determining that there are ranges where the hypothesis is most likely to break down, and examinations of some of them have also found nothing.

Apart from numerical examinations of this kind, there are more theoretical reasons for believing it. We saw above that Riemann made use of the functional equation for the zeta function. There are many settings in mathematics where functions turn up, called L-functions, that have properties like the zeta function. The first, which Dirichlet called the function L because logarithms were involved in his analysis of it, was connected with his magnificent result that every arithmetic progression
$$a, a + b, a + 2b, \ldots, a + kb, \ldots,$$
where a and b are coprime, contains infinitely many prime numbers. Quite generally, L-functions satisfy a functional equation, so an analogue of the Riemann hypothesis can be formulated for them—and proven! This makes the truth of the original Riemann hypothesis seem very likely. However, there are cases where the analogy breaks down, and this leaves room for the more skeptical

mathematician to argue that the Riemann hypothesis will be another exception.

The same thing happens when dealing with what are called finite fields. A field in mathematics is a set of objects that can be added, subtracted, multiplied, and divided, and in which addition and multiplication are both commutative. A finite field is a field with only finitely many elements, and they can have only a specific range of sizes: the number of elements in any finite field is a power of a prime number.

Simple examples are the remainders modulo a prime. For example, any integer divided by 5 leaves a remainder of either 0, 1, 2, 3, or 4. These remainders form a field, and one has such results as $3 + 4 = 2, 3 \times 3 = 4$, and so on.

There are many reasons to study finite fields. These days, coding of electronic signals for communication—everything from phone calls to banking transactions—is a major one. But another is the study of one of the oldest questions in mathematics: when is a polynomial equation satisfied by integers? For example $y^3 = x^2 + 2$ is satisfied when $x = 5$ and $y = 3$, but by no other positive integers

Finite fields enter the study of this type of question in an obvious way. Confronted with the question: "Are there integers that satisfy the equation $y^2 = 5x^2 + 2$?" we can observe that if there were, then taking remainders modulo 5, there would be integers y such that y^2 leaves a remainder of 2 on division by 5. But it is easy to see that all squares on division by 5 leave remainders of 0, 1, or 4. So there are no such integers <y and so no solutions in integers to $y^2 = 5x^2 + 2$.

A whole branch of number theory exploits the fact that it is possible to formulate an analogy of the Riemann hypothesis in the theory of finite fields, and one of the mathematical triumphs of the late 20th century was Pierre Deligne's proof that this form of the Riemann hypothesis can be proven. This is more evidence that the original version might also hold, without being conclusive.

There are other straws in the wind in the form of results that were first proven on the assumption that the Riemann hypothesis is correct and have since been established without it. There are other theoretical settings in which the original Riemann hypothesis can be formulated; currently, a connection with quantum mechanics and what are called random matrices is receiving a lot of attention. But the conjecture has had its 162nd birthday, and has resisted many attempts by leading mathematicians to prove it. That fact alone has made many mathematicians think that the Riemann hypothesis is false. Perhaps one day we shall find out for sure.

Minimal surfaces

The study of minimal surfaces sits in the overlap between analysis and geometry. The area of a surface is expressed mathematically as an integral, and analysts are always interested when a function or an integral takes a maximal or minimal value.

Some examples are classical. What is the shortest piece of string that encloses a given area? The answer is when the area is in the shape of a disc, and the string is the boundary circle. To put the same problem another way: what is the largest area you can enclose with a given piece of string?

In this spirit, it is natural to ask what the surface of least area that passes through a given curve in space is? As we saw above, Riemann was the first to propose a general plan of attack on this problem.

Geometers take their lead from Meusnier, who showed that a surface of least area has the attractive property of being a surface of zero mean curvature. Such surfaces are everywhere saddle-shaped.

Riemann's approach was that of an analyst, and it yielded a formula for parameterizing least area surfaces. At almost the same time, Weierstrass took his cue from geometry and came to a very similar result about zero mean curvature surfaces. But neither man had a way of fitting a minimal surface to a given curve in space, unless the curve was very simple, typically made up of a finite number of line segments.

A spirited but subtly flawed account of the problem for an

arbitrary smooth curve in space was given by René Garnier in the 1920s. It built on this earlier work, but it was almost immediately eclipsed by the new ideas of Tibor Radó in Europe and Jesse Douglas in the United States.

In 1930-31, Radó showed that any continuous curve in space spanning at least one surface of finite area, spans a surface of least area. At the same time, Douglas showed that any curve in space spans a minimal surface, that various combinations of curves span a minimal surface, and that the topological type of the surface can sometimes be specified in advance (when there is only one boundary curve to be spanned, we can ask that it be a Möbius band, for example, rather than a disc). Among the curves admitted by his theory are ones that span no surface of finite area, but they span surfaces that are minimal away from the boundary. For this discovery, he was awarded one of the first two Fields Medals at the International Congress of Mathematicians in Oslo in 1936.

Douglas's methods have largely been replaced, but his program—to show that given any combination of curves in space, and any compatible topological structure on the space of spanning surfaces, either there is a minimal spanning surface of that type or there are simple reasons there cannot be (as with the two circles and the catenoid)—has been almost completely vindicated. Only in the last few years, however, have examples been found for a variety of cases, so that computers can draw them and we can see what Douglas was the first to prove.

To an analyst, the existence of minimal surfaces is a problem in the theory of partial differential equations, and this theory leans heavily on examples. The partial differential equation that is satisfied by a minimal surface is a propitious example because it makes good geometrical sense, and it can be generalized to any number of variables. This has yielded remarkable results. There are also many cases in mathematics where one has a manifold of some dimension and a class of submanifolds satisfying a particular condition. A natural question to ask is if there is a best one of these submanifolds, such as the smallest, and this has been another valuable query.

Real functions

Real analysis is the largest branch of mathematics, embracing many substantial subfields, so it is unwise to attribute major developments to a single person. That said, Riemann's introduction of trigonometric series broke open what until then had been at the edge of mathematicians' awareness: the existence of functions that are not differentiable, and perhaps not even integrable.

The study of Fourier series that are not faithful representations of functions steadily deepened, and the results were remarkable. In the 1870s, Georg Cantor took up the question of whether the Fourier series representation was unique. If not, the difference between two representations of a given function must be a representation of the zero function—but how could this be?

Cantor saw that the answer lay in a study of points on the real line where the representation breaks down; let us call them "bad" points for the moment. He investigated sets of bad points. Could they be single points? He found they could. A bad set could be a finite set of points. It could also be infinite sets of points that were scattered—each point separated from the others by an interval of some size. This led him to think about all the points P that were so close to a bad set that any interval containing P also contained points of the bad set. He called these new points P the limit set of the bad set. It too could be bad. What about the limit set of a limit set? It could be bad as well. And so on, all the way to the limit set of a limit set of a limit set of a .... Cantor even realized that you could start with such a set, and form its limit set, and go on again.

He found it helpful to count the number of times he had formed a limit set, so starting from a set P^0 he called its limit set P^1, the limit set of P^1 he called P^2, and so on. He called the limit set of a limit set of a limit set of a ... obtained by forming the limit set infinitely many times the set P^ω. But you might be given a set Q and not know it had been obtained in this way. You could innocently form its limit set Q^1. So if in fact $Q = P^\omega$, then $Q^1 = P^{\omega+1}$. Its limit set would be $Q^2 = P^{\omega+2}$ and so on.

Of course, we must ask if this process does anything more than hand out multiple names for the same object. It's a bit of work, which Cantor did not do, to find a set P so that $P \neq P^1 \neq P^2$ .... But they exist, for example, the zero sets of $\sin(1/x), \sin(1/\sin(1/x)), \ldots$ are sets of type $1, 2, \ldots, n, \ldots$, as the mathematician Paul Du Bois-Reymond showed in a paper in 1875.

Cantor worked on these ideas for a few years, then moved on to other topics, and then came back in the late 1870s. Now he saw something very interesting, not about the sets but about the numbers. They went

$$0, 1, 2, 3, \ldots, \omega, \omega + 1, \omega + 2, \ldots, 2\omega, 2\omega + 1, 2\omega + 2, \ldots,$$

and as a sequence, they never stopped. They were a natural continuation of the way we count:

after the zeroth set, we get the first new set, the second one, and so on. But now we break through into a realm of infinite sets. Cantor had discovered a way of talking about infinite sets of different kinds.

If we look for a set associated with ω a natural candidate is the set of natural numbers $1, 2, 3, \ldots, n$ in this order. But it is far from unique. We might for some reason list the natural numbers in a different order, such as $2, 1, 3, 4, \ldots$, or $1, 3, 5, 2, 7, 9, 11, 4, \ldots$. But what if we place 2 right at the end, listing them this way: $1, 3, 4, 5, \ldots, 2$, so 2 comes after every other natural number? This is a natural candidate for set corresponding to the new number $\omega + 1$. In this way, we see that $\omega + 1$ is not the same as $1 + \omega$, and indeed $1 + \omega = \omega$. Similarly, a natural candidate for $\omega + 2$ is $1, 3, 5, \ldots, 2, 4$, and natural candidates for other new numbers can be found in the same way.

What if we put all the odd positive numbers before all the even ones, and consider

$$1, 3, 5, \ldots, 2, 4, 6, \ldots?$$

That is a natural candidate for $\omega + \omega = 2\omega$. And what about this way of listing the natural numbers, which was connected to the study of iteration and chaos in the 1990s:

$$3, 5, 7, \ldots, 6, 10, 14, \ldots, 12, 20, 28, \ldots, 32, 16, 8, 4, 2, 1?$$

This has infinitely many sequences, each containing infinitely many natural numbers, so it is a natural candidate to represent $\omega \times \omega$, or ω^2.

Cantor's discovery of the domain of infinite sets was one of the great discoveries of mathematics. It ended millennia of believing that it was only possible to talk about finite sizes and one unique thing that was larger than any finite set, called the potential infinite. It ushered in the move to base all of mathematics on a theory of sets, which was carried out in the early decades of the 20th century.

Riemann's insight that there are many functions with unexpected, counter-intuitive properties paved the way to the idea that the theory of the integral needed an overhaul. Strictly speaking, Riemann's contribution to the theory of the integral consisted only in making precise what Cauchy had done in the 1820s, but that made it easier to find the limits of the theory.

In fact, integration and differentiation had had an uneasy history since their discovery by Newton and Leibniz and formed the basis of many earlier ideas. Differentiation was connected with finding the tangent to a given curve at a given point on it; integration was connected with finding the area under a curve. Newton and Leibniz realized that in some sense, these processes were mutually inverse. In the language of functions, rather than curves, if we integrate a function and then differentiate, we get the function back, and if we differentiate a function and then integrate, we get the function back plus an arbitrary constant. Both men, and everyone else who took up the calculus, also realized that differentiation is easy and integration can be hard.

This opened up two ways of proceeding: we could keep the two processes, and establish their inverse relationship as a theorem, the Fundamental Theorem of the Calculus; or we could simply define integration as the inverse of differentiation. Mathematicians of the 18th century took the second option, and Cauchy swung people back to the first. However, with the profusion of strange functions in the late 19th century, people began to ask if the Fundamental Theorem of the Calculus was correct. As perhaps you have begun to suspect, it was not.

This problem drew attention to a weakness of Riemann's theory of the integral: a sequence of integrable functions $f_n(x)$ can tend to an integrable function $f(x)$, and yet it can fail to be the case that the sequence of integrals $\int f_n(x)dx$ tends to the integral $\int f(x)dx$. Worse still, the limit function may not even be integrable (on Riemann's definition) so a new definition of the integral is needed.

Several modifications and alternatives to it were proposed, and the most useful suggestion by far came from the French mathematician Henri Lebesgue in 1902 and 1904. His theory does not have the weakness just described, and very quickly, it acquired a use that even Lebesgue could not have expected. It works very well when one is studying spaces of functions, and sequences of functions are in play. The surprise was that it turned out to be just the right setting for the mathematics of quantum mechanics.

Lebesgue's theory, like any theory of integration, is about the size of sets, and there is another arena where sizes of sets are at stake: probability theory. Every time we ask what the likelihood of a particular outcome among a whole set of possible outcomes is, we are comparing two sets. Thus, Lebesgue's theory of the integral is the right theory for a rigorous account of probability, something that was accomplished for the first time in the 1930s by the Soviet mathematician Andrei Kolmogorov.

Surprisingly, it took a long time for pure mathematicians interested in real analysis and probability theories to realize that they were talking about the same thing from different points of view. But their recognition, like many such, has been particularly fruitful, and seems likely to be one of the major topics for research in the 21st century.

References

H ere are the works and authors I have referred to throughout this book:

Beltrami, E. 1868. Saggio di interpretazione della geometria non–euclidea, *Giornale di Matematiche* 6, 285–315, in *Opere Matematiche* 1, 374–405.

Bolyai, J. 1832, Appendix scientiam spatii absolute veram exhibens, in Farkas Bolyai, *Tentamen juventutem studiosam in Elementa Matheosis purae*, etc., Maros-Vàsérhely, 1832. English transl. G. B. Halsted, Science Absolute of Space, Appendix in (Gray 2004).

Bombieri, E. 2006. The Riemann hypothesis, *The Millennium Prize Problems*, J. Carlson, A. Jaffe, and A. Wiles (eds.) 107–124.

Bonnet, O. 1848. Mémoire sur la théorie générale des surfaces, *Journal de l'École Polytechnique* 19, 1–146.

Bottazzini, U. 1999. Ricci and Levi-Civita: from differential invariants to general relativity, *The Symbolic Universe*, J.J. Gray (ed.) 241–259, Oxford U.P.

Bottazzini, U. and R. Tazzioli. 1995. Naturphilosophie and its role in Riemann's mathematics, *Revue d'histoire des mathématiques* 1, 3–38.

Bottazzini, U. and J.J. Gray, 2013. *Hidden Harmony–Geometric Fantasies; The rise of complex function theory*, Springer.

Bühler, W.K. 1981. *Gauss: A Biographical Study*, Springer.

Cantor, G. 1870a. Über einen die trigonometrischen Reihen betreffenden Lehrsatz, *Journal für die reine und angewandte Mathematik* 72, 130–138 in *Gesammelte Abhandlungen*, 71–79.

Cantor, G. 1870b. Beweis, dass eine für jeden reellen Wert von x durch eine trigonometrische Reihe gegebene function $f(x)$ [etc]. *Journal für die reine und angewandte Mathematik* 72, 139–142, in *Gesammelte Abhandlungen*, 80–83.

Cantor, G. 1883. *Grundlagen einer allgemeinen Mannigfaltigkeitslehre*, Teubner, Leipzig.

Carlson, J., A. Jaffe, and A. Wiles (eds.), 2006. *The Millennium Prize Problems*, Clay Mathematical Institute and American Mathematical Society.

Christoffel, E.B. 1869. Über die Transformation der homogenen Differentialausdrücke zweiten Grades, *Journal für die reine und angewandte Mathematik* 70, 46–70.

Christoffel, E.B. 1870. Ueber die Abbildung einer einblättrigen, einfach zusammenhängenden, ebenen Fläche auf einem Kreise, *Göttingen Nachr.* 283–298, in *Gesammelte Mathematische Abhandlungen*, 9–18. Krazer, A. and G. Faber (eds.) Teubner, Leipzig and Berlin.

Darboux, G. 1887–1893. *Lecons sur la Théorie générale des Surfaces*, Paris, Gauthier-Villars (2nd ed. 1914).

Dedekind, R. 1876. Bernhard Riemann's Lebenslauf, in (Riemann 1990, 573–590) and (Riemann 2004, 518–534).

Dirichlet, P.G.L. 1828. Mémoire sur l'impossibilité de quelques équations indéterminées du cinquième degré, *Journal für die reine und angewandte Mathematik* 3, 354–375, in *Werke* 1, 21–46.

Dirichlet, P.G.L. 1829. Sur la convergence des séries trigonométriques qui servent à représenter une fonction arbitraire entre des limites données. *Journal für die reine und angewandte Mathematik* 4, 157–169, in *Werke* 1, 117–132.

Dirichlet, P.G.L. 1837b. Beweis des Satzes, dass jede unbegrenzte arithmetische Progression [etc]. *Berlin Abhandlungen* 45–81 in *Werke* 1, 313–342.

Douglas, J. 1931. Solution of the Problem of Plateau, *Transactions of the American Mathematical Society* 32.1, 263–321.

Dunnington, G.W. 1955/2004. *Gauss–Titan of Science*, introduction and appendices J.J. Gray, Mathematical Association of America.

Einstein, A. and M. Grossmann, 1914. Entwurf einer verallgemeinerten Relativitätstheorie und einer Theorie der Gravitation, *Zeitschrift für Mathematik und Physik* 62, 225–261, in *Collected Papers of Albert Einstein* 4, Doc. 13, M.J. Klein, A.J. Kox, J. Renn, R. Schulmann (eds.) Princeton University Press.

Einstein, A. 1916 *Die Grundlagen der allgemeinen Relativitätstheorie*, Leipzig, English transl. R.W. Lawson, *Relativity: The Special and General Theory*, Methuen, London, 1920, many subsequent editions.

Euler, L. 1767. Recherches sur la courbure des surfaces, *Histoire de l'académie des sciences de Berlin* 16, 119—143, in *Opera Omnia* (ser. 1), 28, 1—22 (E333).

Euler, L. 1775. De repraesentatione superficiei sphaericae super plano, *Acta Acad. Sci. Imp. Petrop.* (1777—1778), 107—132, in *Opera Omnia* (ser. 1), 28, 248—275 (E490).

Fourier, J. 1822. *Théorie analytique de la Chaleur.* Firmin Didot, Paris in *Oeuvres* 1. Rep. Gabay, Paris 1988. English transl. A. Freeman, *The Analytical Theory of Heat*, Cambridge U.P. 1878. Repr. Dover, New York 1950.

Gauss, C.F. 1822a. Allgemeine Auflösung der Aufgabe die Theile einer gegebenen Fläche auf einer andern gegebenen Fläche so abzubilden, dass die Abbildung dem Abgebildeten in den kleinisten Theilen ähnlich wird, *Astronomische Abhandlungen*, 3, 1825, in Gauss, *Werke* IV, 1880, 189—216.

Gauss, C.F. 1822b. Stand meiner Untersuchung über die Umformung der Flächen, first published in Gauss *Werke* VIII, 374—384.

Gauss, C.F. 1827a. Disquisitiones generales circa superficies curvas rep. in *Werke* IV, 217—258, Latin original with a reprint of the English translation by A. Hiltebeitel and J. Morehead 1902 repr. P. Dombrowski (ed.) in *astérisque* 62, 1979, 1—81, and as *General investigations of curved surfaces*, P. Pesic, (ed.) Dover Books, New York,

Gauss, C.F. 1827b. Anzeige to Disquisitiones generales circa superficies curvas in *Werke* IV, 341—346, in (Gauss 1827a, 45—51).

Gray, J.J. 1989. *Ideas of Space, Euclidean, non-Euclidean and Relativistic*, 2nd edn., Oxford University Press.

Gray, J.J, 2004. *Janos Bolyai, non-Euclidean Geometry and the Nature of Space*, Burndy Library, M.I.T. Press.

Gray, J.J. 2011. *Worlds out of Nothing; A Course on the History of Geometry in the 19th Century*, 2nd edn., Springer.

Hadamard, J. 1896. Sur la distribution des zéros de la fonction et ses conséquences arithmétiques, *Bulletin de la Société Mathématique de France*, 24, 199–220, in Oeuvres 1, 189–210.

Hankel H. 1870. Untersuchungen über die unendlich oft oscillirenden und unstetigen Functionen, *Gratulationprogramm der Tübinger Universität*. Repr. *Mathematische Annalen* 20 (1882), 63–112.

Herbart, J.F. 1824–1825. *Psychologie als Wissenschaft neu gegrundet auf Erfahrung, Metaphysik, und Mathematik*. 2 vols.

Lagrange, J.L. 1761. Essai d'une nouvelle méthode pour déterminer les maxima et minima des formules intégrales indéfinies, *Miscellanea Taurenensia* 2, 173–196, in *Oeuvres de Lagrange*, 1, Gauthier-Villars, Paris, 1867, 335–362.

Lambert, J.H. 1772. Anmerkungen und Zusätze zur Entwerfung der Land- und Himmelscharten, *Beiträge zum Gebraucheder Mathematik und deren Anwendung*, Part 3, Berlin, 105–199.

Laugwitz, D. 1996. *Bernhard Riemann 1826–1866. Wendepunkte in der Auffassung der Mathematik*. Birkhäuser, Basel. English transl. A. Shenitzer, *Riemann 1826–1866: Turning points in the conception of mathematics*. Birkhäuser, Boston 1999.

Lebesgue, H. 1902. Intégrale, longueur, aire, *Annali di Matematiche* (3) 7, 231–359 in *Oeuvres scientifiques* 1, 203–331.

Lebesgue, H. 1904. *Leçons sur l'intégration et la recherche des fonctions primitives*, Gauthier–Villars, Paris, in *Oeuvres scientifiques* 2, 11–154. Rep. Gabay, Paris 1989 and AMS Chelsea, New York 2003.

Levi-Civita, T. 1893. Sugli invarianti assolutti, *Atti Istituto Veneto* 5, 1447–1523, in *Opere Matematiche* 1, 41–100.

Lipschitz, R. 1870a. Entwickelung einiger Eigenschaften der quadratischen Formen von n Differentialen, *Journal für die reine und angewandte Mathematik* 71, 274–287 and 288–295.

Lipschitz, R. 1870b. Fortgesetzte Untersuchungen in Betreff der ganzen homogenen Functionen von n Differentialen, *Journal für die reine und angewandte Mathematik* 72, 1–56.

Lobachevskii, N.I. 1840. *Geometrische Untersuchungen*, Berlin, rep. Mayer & Müller, 1887, Eng. tr. G. B. Halsted, Geometric Researches in the Theory of Parallels, Appendix in (Bonola 1912). See also S. Braver, *Lobachevski Illuminated*, Mathematical Association of America, Washington DC, 2011.

Meusnier, J.B. 1785. Mémoire sur la courbure des surfaces, *Mémoires mathématiques et physiques des savants étrangers* 10, 477−510.

Minkowski, H. 1908. Raum und Zeit, *Jahrsbericht den Deutschen mathematiker Vereinigung* 75−88, in *Gesammelte Abhandlungen* 2, 431−444, English transl. in The Principle of Relativity, A. Sommerfeld (ed.), Dover rep. 1952, 73−91.

Monge, G. 1807. *Applications d'analyse à la géométrie* 5th ed. 1850, Bachelier, Paris, 5me édition, revue, corrigée et annotée par M. Liouville, Paris.

Odlyzko, A.M. The zero of the Riemann zeta function, in *Dynamical, Spectral, and Arithmetic Zeta Functions*, M. van Frankenhuysen and M. L. Lapidus, eds., American Mathematical Society, Contemporary Math. series, no. 290, 2001, pp. 139−144.

Plateau, J. 1873. *Statique expérimentale et théorique des liquides soumis aux seules forces moléculaires*, two vols. Paris, Gauthier-Villars.

Riemann, G.F.B. 1851. Grundlagen für eine allgemeine Theorie der Functionen einer veränderlichen complexen Grösse, *Inauguraldissertation*, Göttingen, in (Riemann 1990, 1−43) and (Riemann 2004, 1−42).

Riemann, G.F.B. 1854a/1867. Über die Darstellbarkeit einer Function durch einer trigonometrische Reihe, *K. Ges. Wiss. Göttingen*, 13, 87−132, in (Riemann 1990, 259−297) and (Riemann 2004, 219−256).

Riemann, G.F.B. 1854b/1867. Ueber die Hypothesen welche der Geometrie zu Grunde liegen, *K. Ges. Wiss. Göttingen*, 13, 1−20, in (Riemann 1990, 304−319) and (Riemann 2004, 257−272).

Riemann, G.F.B. 1857. Theorie der Abel'schen Functionen, *Journal für die reine und angewandte Mathematik* 54, 101–155, in (Riemann 1990, 120–174) and (Riemann 2004, 79–134).

Riemann, G.F.B. 1859. Ueber die Anzahl der Primzahlen unter einer gegebene Grösse, *Monatsberichte Berlin*, 671–680, in (Riemann 1990, 177–187) and (Riemann 2004, 135–144).

Riemann, G.F.B. 1867. Ueber die Fläche vom kleinsten Inhalt bei gegebener Begrenzung. (ed. K. Hattendorf) *Göttingen Abhandlungen* 13, in (Riemann 1990, 333–365) and (Riemann 2004, 287–322).

Riemann, G.F.B. 1990. *Gesammelte Mathematische Werke*, 3rd ed. R. Narasimhan, Springer, New York.

Riemann, G.F.B. 2004. *Collected Papers*, English transl. R. Baker, C. Christenson, H. Orde, Kendrick Press.

Ricci-Curbastro, G. 1886. Sui parametri e gli invarianti delle forme quadratiche differenziali. *Annali di Matematiche*, (2) 1, 1-11, in *Opere* 1, 177–188.

Scholz, E. 1982a. Riemann's frühe Notizen zum Mannigfaltigkeitsbegriff und zu den Grundlagen der Geometrie, *Archive for History of Exact Sciences*, 27, 213–232.

Scholz, E. 1982b. Herbart's influence on Bernhard Riemann, *Historia Mathematica* 9, 413–440.

Schwarz, H.A. 1865. Ueber die Minimalfläche, deren Begrenzung als ein von vier Kanten eines regulären Tetraeders gebildetes räumliches Viersiet gegeben ist. Im April 1865 von Herrn Kummer der Königlichen Akademie der Wissenschaften zu Berlin mitgetheilt. *Monatsberichte der Königlichen Akademie der Wissenchaften zu Berlin*, 149–153, in *Gesammelte Mathematische Abhandlungen* 1, 1–5, Berlin.

Schwarz, H.A. 1885. Über ein die Flächen kleinsten Flächeninhalts betreffendes Problem der Variationsrechnung. Festschrift zum siebzigsten Geburtstage des Herrn Karl Weierstrass, *Acta societatis scientiarum Fennicae* 15, 315–362, in *Gesammelte Mathematische Abhandlungen* 1, 223–269, Berlin.

Schweikart, F.K. 1818. Notiz, in Gauss *Werke* 8, 175–176.

Vallée Poussin, Ch. de la, 1896. Recherches analytiques sur la théorie des nombres premiers, *Annales de la Société Scientifiques,* Bruxelles 20, 83—256 and 281—297.

Weyl, H. 1913. *Die Idee der Riemannschen Fläche,* Teubner, Leipzig. 2nd edn. Teubner, Leipzig 1926. 3rd revised edn. Teubner, Stuttgart 1955. English transl. of 3rd edn. as *The Concept of a Riemann surface,* 1955, repr. Dover, New York, 2009.

Weierstrass, K. 1866a. Untersuchungen über die Flächen, deren mittlere Krümmung überall gleich Null ist, Umarbeitung einer am 25. Juni 1866 in der Akademie der Wissenschaften zu Berlin gelesen, in der *Monatsberichte der Akademie,* 1866 (pub. 1867), 612—625, auszugeweise abgedruckten Abhandlung, in *Werke* 3, 1903, 39—52.

Suggested Reading

Many of Riemann's best ideas were naïve—geometry is about lengths, complex functions are functions on surfaces, wildly behaved functions should fit badly into a theory of Fourier series. Like most simple ideas, they require a lot of detailed work if they are to prove significant. Other ideas of his, such as his analysis of the distribution of prime numbers, were difficult from the start. Either way, the gap from his challenging insights to a rigorous modern theory was wide, and it does not result in books that are readable outside of a university course. However, such was their significance that several excellent books illuminate what Riemann achieved and why it has continued to matter.

Umberto Bottazzini's *The Higher Calculus*, Springer (1986), is a very good historical introduction to the history of analysis and it more than covers the topics discussed here.

John Derbyshire's *Prime Obsession*, Joseph Henry Press (2003), is a very good introduction to the Riemann hypothesis, as is the book by Barry Mazur and William Stein, *Prime Numbers and the Riemann Hypothesis*, Cambridge University Press (2018), which covers many related subjects with an abundance of stimulating diagrams.

My own *Plato's Ghost: The Modernist Transformation of Mathematics*, Princeton University Press (2008), argues the case that mathematics underwent a modernist transformation, much of it driven by the impact of Riemann's ideas. Readers wanting to know more about geometry in the 19thcentury can also consult my *Worlds out of Nothing*, Springer (2nd revised edn. 2011).

Detlef Laugwitz's biography *Bernhard Riemann*, Birkhäuser (1996) covers the life and the continuing importance of Riemann's work.

John Stillwell's *Geometry of Surfaces*, Springer (1992) is the most readable rigorous introduction to the subject, from a topological point of view. I know of no book on differential geometry that is accessible to the general reader which is a shame because it is highly visual and exciting.

About the Author

Jeremy Gray is Professor Emeritus at the Open University in the U.K. and an Honorary Professor in the Department of Mathematics at the University of Warwick. A specialist in the history of mathematics in the 19th and early 20th centuries, he is the author of *Henri Poincaré: a Scientific Biography*, Princeton University Press (2012); (with Umberto Bottazzini, Milan) *Hidden Harmony—Geometric Fantasies: The Rise of Complex Function Theory*, Springer (2013); and *A History of Abstract Algebra*, Springer (2018), among other titles. Professor Gray is a fellow of the American Mathematical Society and received their Albert Leon Whiteman Memorial Prize in 2009 for his work on the history of mathematics. He was awarded the Neugebauer Prize of the European Mathematical Society in 2016.

A Word from the Publisher

Thank you for reading *Simply Riemann*!

If you enjoyed reading it, we would be grateful if you could help others discover and enjoy it too.

Please review it with your favorite book provider such as Amazon, BN, Kobo, Apple Books, or Goodreads, among others.

Again, thank you for your support and we look forward to offering you more great reads.

Printed in Great Britain
by Amazon

59250309R00097